MAKE-UP
Colours and Style

foulsham

LONDON • NEW YORK • TORONTO • SYDNEY

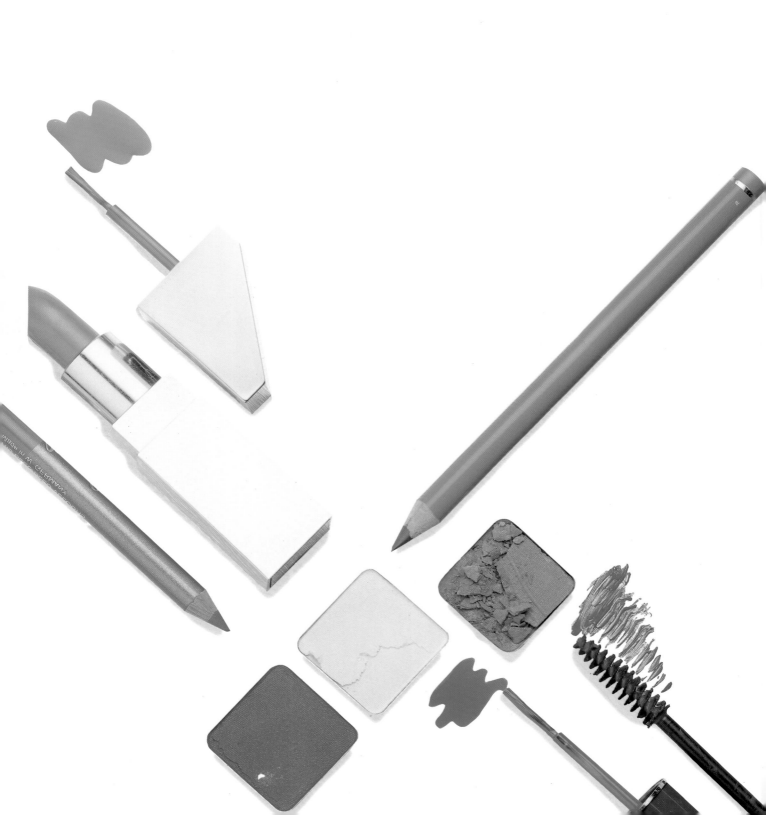

MAKE-UP
Colours and Style

Top professional tips for everyone

by Margaret Rüdiger

foulsham

The Publishing House, Bennetts Close,
Cippenham, Berkshire, SL1 5AP, England.

ISBN 0-572-02052-X

This English language edition copyright © 1996 W Foulsham & Co Ltd.
Originally published by Falken Verlag GmbH, 6272 Niedernhausen/Ts, Germany
in association with **freundin**
Photographs © Falken-Verlag.
Photographs supplied by: Otto Rauser S.; freundin-Archiv. S.;
Michael Leis; Hannelore Hopp. S.; Manfred Spachmann. S.;
Hans Georg Gessner/ALCINA. S.; Peter Pfander. S.;
Antje Pesel; Yvonne Kranz; Lars Matzen;
Lorenz Zatrecky; Herbert Brehm; Arne Bockelmann;
Gerald Klepka; Kai Mahrholz; Thomas von Salomon. S.;
Martin Brandis; Karl Bessinger.

Professional beauticians Horst Kirchenberger and Gesine Margenberg (pages 8 and 9)

Printed in Great Britain by Cambus Litho, East Kilbride.

Make-up is not a mask; nor is it just a question of fashion. Make-up is the art of discovering the best features of your face and accentuating your individuality – whether we are talking about pouting lips, 'cat's eyes' or false eyelashes. Although most people tend to keep up to date with fashion trends, this is not essential if the object is to look good, appear well-groomed and radiate self-confidence. What is vital is that you understand how to make the best of your looks, and to do that, you must start by defining your natural colour. Are you a Spring, Summer, Autumn or Winter type? Discover that, and your perfect colour palette follows naturally.

Of course, make-up can also send out erotic signals – look here, here is someone who likes herself and wants to be liked! This is one reason why make-up has always been used, mostly by women – but also by men!

This book offers a basic course in make-up techniques and explains everything you need to know about appropriate preparations and untensils. The latest information is combined with timeless advice. Those already competent in using make-up will discover something new, and those with only a little experience will learn the most important techniques, all beautifully illustrated so you can see the effects for yourself.

*Make-up products and techniques
for the best looks.*

Step by step to great make-up looks.

The best way to look after your skin.

CHAPTER 1

The right colours   10

Finding your colour type   12

Spring type   14

Summer type   18

Autumn type   22

Winter type   26

CHAPTER 2

From foundation to lipstick   30

Basic equipment   32

Foundation   34

Powder   40

The eyebrows   44

Contouring   48

Blusher   50

Eyeshadow   54

Eyeliner   60

The eyelashes   64

The lips   68

CHAPTER 3

Super make-up step by step   74

Natural make-up   76

Evening make-up   80

Make-up for work   84

Quick make-up   88

CHAPTER 4

Skin care and protection	**90**
Skin care	**92**
What to buy	**100**
Extra tips	**102**

Solutions to common make-up problems.

CHAPTER 5

Tricks for solving problems	**106**
Hidden eyelids	**108**
Small eyes	**109**
Thin lips	**110**
Full lips	**111**
Freckles	**112**
Pale skin	**113**
Make-up with glasses	**114**
Shape of the face	**116**

*Choosing and using the right colours
for your seasonal type.*

CHAPTER 6

Make-up for every occasion	**120**
Sunbathing	**122**
Winter sports	**123**
Weekends	**124**
Water sports	**126**
Fitness training	**127**

*Swimming, jogging or partying –
make-up for every occasion.*

Index	**128**

All the professional tips and explanations of correct techniques in this book have been provided by professional make-up artists, who have many years experience in the fashion and cosmetics industries.

Find out what the professionals think about make-up and learn their own make-up secrets.

How important is make-up, should it be 'fashionable' and how can you use it to make you beautiful?

We asked the experts for their opinions.

INTRODUCTION

Question: What do you understand by being beautiful?

Answers: "Something external that harmonises with the person's life and allows their personality to shine – certainly not an applied 'look'."

"I find a women beautiful when you look at her and see that she is happy with herself and the effect she has on others."

Question: What role does make-up play in this sort of beauty?

Answers: "Something playful. Make-up should give a woman the certainty that her facial assets are unmistakable and anything that could be construed as a defect is seen as an individual characteristic."

The professional beautician applies make-up in international photographic studios and in his own make-up advice institute.

"For me, on the one hand, make-up has to do with mood; on the other, with self-assurance. By mood I mean that make-up should only be used when you feel like it, and done in a way that expresses this impulse and does not slavishly follow fashion. On the other hand, I agree that a routine and a certain amount of skill is helpful when using make-up. It is a tremendous advantage to be able to apply make-up with the same ease as choosing the clothes which suit you best from your wardrobe. And practice makes perfect!"

Question: What is the most important thing about make-up?

Answers: "The skill with which the make-up is applied. The most important thing is not that everything is well-covered, because this usually looks very unnatural. Above all, the skin must look transparent, despite make-up and powder; the colour must be right."

"The most important thing for me, besides a quiet, even skin tone and a fresh, well-placed blusher is that the eyes should appear natural and not plastered with make-up."

Question: How important is it to you that make-up is fashionable?

Answers: "Not at all important. My advice is always geared to the particular person, with their own individual colour and shape in mind."

"The most common mistake that women make is that they follow a fashion rather than a type. I find nothing wrong if a woman finds a style which suits her, sticks with it and then experiments as she fancies."

Question: And you – do you use make-up?

Answers: "For years I have used self-tan and a terracotta powder, because I look better and healthier without having to lie in the sun. Generally everyone I reveal this secret to is surprised, as they would never have guessed it."

"When working I hardly use any make-up. If I want to make myself look pretty, then I use terracotta powder, mascara and lipstick. The reason for this is over-availability of everything relating to make-up, but also because I am a sporty type. Nothing else really suits me and so I don't use lavish make-up, just enough to be seen. Then people think 'She knows how to use make-up'!"

The professional make-up artist makes up models for fashion and cosmetic photographs for magazines and advertising agents.

CHAPTER I

The right colours

- **Finding your colour type**
- **Colour types and their characteristics**
- **Ideal make-up for every type**
- **The correct make-up colours**

FINDING YOUR COLOUR TYPE

■ Everyone has a natural affinity with the colours of one of the four seasons, and will look their best when their make-up is attuned to those tones. Look through this chapter to get a feel for the colour palettes for each season, then work through to identify your colour type.

Remember, once you have identified your season you can use this knowledge forever – you don't usually change from one type to another!

Follow these simple rules:

■ *Remove all your make-up and wear a simple, neutral top.*

■ *Sit in front of a large mirror under good, natural light (other lights will distort your natural colouring).*

■ *Take a good, long look at yourself – what do you see? Make a note of your natural hair colour, your natural eye colour, eyebrow colours, complexion, cheeks, lips and eyelashes. Really observe yourself.*

■ *Then jot down the colours you prefer and which suit you best - in clothes and make-up. What colours are you wearing when you receive the most compliments about your looks?*

■ *Now look at the basic colour characteristics for each seasonal type and the seasonal colour ranges on the colour swatch. You are probably already moving towards your season.*

■ *Remember: although some colours will suit you better than others - that is a part of your unique personality - there is a shade of every colour which you can wear in your clothes. Even if you think red is not your colour there is a red that will suit you. The effect of make-up colours is more subtle, however, so you need to think carefully about specific tones.*

■ *Compare the colours on the colour swatch. Try not to look at the seasonal definitions until you have assessed the effect of the colours on your complexion. For example, when assessing red, take the four different shades and hold them up to your face one at a time. Does one drain colour away from your skin? Does another make your cheeks appear flushed? What one shows off your hair and skin to the best advantage?*

■ *Now follow the same procedure with all the other colours. Ideally all the colours you have chosen will fall within one seasonal palette. But this is not always the case. Think of the colour ranges as spreading around a circle, with each quarter representing the seasons. Your unique colour palette or 'aura' may fall anywhere around the circle.*

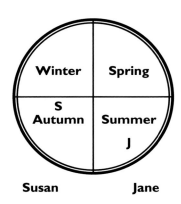

Jane (J) may find it easy to assess that she is a Summer colour type;

Susan (S) may find that she is not sure about some colours.

■ *Once you have chosen your colour season you will find within it some colours which suit you better than others, so think about this carefully before you turn your thoughts to make-up in particular.*

And of course your mood and the occasion in question will demand different make-up treatments.

■ *Experiment with a group of friends. Take a pile of clothes or scarves and analyse and compare the effects the colours have on your skin. Enjoy learning about colours – you will soon discover those which make the best of your looks.*

For the Spring type, a harsh colour contrast is unflattering to the naturally delicate appearance, which is complemented by the softer make-up colours in the picture on the right.

Brown powder and rouge on a deeper-toned skin (photo left) may look sporty on the Summer woman, but it is also a little coarse. Finer and more suited to her type is the cooler make-up shown in the photograph on the right.

Anyone with the reddish hair of the classic Autumn type tends towards over- or under-emphasis, choosing either bland, natural colours or extreme effects such as lilac mother-of-pearl (photo left). Full, rich make-up colours, such as those shown on the right, lend this colour type a lot more contour and definition.

A Winter type with such intense natural colours – dark hair and eyes, light complexion – should emphasise these contrasts. In the subdued make-up treatment on the left the effect is boring; in the photo on the right, the effect is much more exciting.

SPRING TYPE

Personal description: delicate, light skin with a golden yellow undertone (no blue-pink tones), often a light yellow peach-pink overtone. Light or dark blonde hair, with a few gold highlights.

Photo left: the most important rule with make-up is to avoid anything that could look like a mask. It's best if foundation looks yellowish and therefore transparent, so that even freckles shine through naturally. Select a rose colour that tends towards yellow for lips and cheeks. Clear pastel shades are pretty for eyeshadow, which can be muted a little with light grey or brown if you don't want to look too colourful. Never use black mascara.

Photo right: typical make-up colours for the spring type – fresh, clear, gentle pastel shades that fade quickly into apricot and salmon pink rather that rose. Coloured mascara!

■ A person's colour type is determined by the natural pigmentation of their complexion, hair and eyes. According to colour typing by the seasons, the Spring and Autumn types move towards warmth and yellowness, the Summer and Winter types more towards coolness and blueness. Suitable colours: fresh and light for Spring, full and heavy for Autumn, muted and smokey for Summer, clear and lively for Winter. In her make-up the Spring woman should emphasise the gentle nature and transparent colours of her type. Anything that covers thickly and makes strong statements is unsuitable.

■ Foundation: fluid and very transparent, ivory or yellowish beige according to the skin colour. In summer it should be a touch browner, as Spring types often tan well in spite of their delicate skin.

■ Blusher: salmon (in summer too), or additional bronze powder in warm brown tones.

■ Lipstick: salmon rose, lobster or coral red, not too thickly applied, or made transparent with colourless gloss.

■ Eyeshadow: as the Spring type usually has light eyes that vary from blue to blue-turquoise, and from grey-green to gold-brown, pastel shades are the prettiest. Colours that are not gentle enough need weakening with transparent powder or light grey powder eyeshadow.

■ Eyeliner/kohl: on no account should black be used; if necessary use grey or brown, although a colour like blue or green is best of all. Very good: white kohl on the lower lid, combined or mixed with a coloured line.

■ Lashes and brows: black is also taboo here. Use a gentle brown on the eyebrows, and possibly paint lines between the hairs with a golden coloured pencil. Mascara in warm (yellowish) blue or green shades suits the Spring type better than any other type.

1

2

3

Not all Spring types are the same, but all have common features: the warm blonde of the hair and the delicacy of the complexion is striking. Spring women should wear dresses in warm pastel colours or choose shades of fresh spring flowers, with rather delicate make-up (see left).

1 *Lipstick, blusher and eyeshadow in salmon rose, brown mascara and a white kohl line on the lower lid.*

2 *The reddish blonde tone of the hair is in harmony with the warm orange of the jacket.*

3 *"Jeans" blue: this is the best colour for Spring types, provided it does not tend too much towards grey (this applies to eyeshadow and clothing).*

4 *Violet blue and bright leaf green - a real Spring combination. The hair is streaked in different warm blond tones.*

5 *Only three colours, but exactly the right ones: blonde, blue and on the lips a salmon colour.*

6 *Eye make-up with powdered pastel colours and a white kohl.*

7 *A successful colour mixture: salmon, light blue and light green eyeshadow, with turquoise mascara.*

8 *May green and dark lilac: strong Spring colours for real Spring types.*

SUMMER TYPE

Personal description: usually very fair, yet sometimes with an olive complexion recognisable by its bluish undertone. Hair colour varies between blonde and brown and always has an ash tone (in contrast to the golden tone of the Spring type).

Photo left: to match the bluish undertone of the skin, foundation should be neutral beige or have a hint of rose. Lipstick and blusher with bluish undertones also suit the Summer type best. Pretty for the eyes: a combination of cool blue, turquoise and violet tones, with muted grey or shiny silver. Charcoal grey mascara is best.

Photo right: neutral beige, cool pink, cool steel blue and muted rose - Summer types will always look right with these colours.

It is difficult for the Summer type to evaluate herself. If looked at superficially her features may appear contradictory and can lead to confusion. For example, the complexion: it can be very fair, soft, rosy and not tan very easily, but it can also have a tinge of olive and take on a cool hazelnut tone in the sun. With a closer look, however, the characteristic bluish undertone is recognisable in both cases, and is complemented by clothes and make-up in cool, often somewhat smokey or milky colours. If the Summer type has freckles, they are grey-brown. Summer types were nearly always blonde as children and only later on grow darker, often 'mousy', to their distress! The eyes are often grey-blue, light blue, petrol grey, blue-green or hazelnut brown.

■ Foundation: the colour choice depends on the skin – whether it has a fair or an olive tone. In the first case very light beige foundation is best, either neutral or with a tinge of rose. For olive-toned skin, a more grey-brown foundation is appropriate.

■ Rouge: a light grey, muted rose is the prettiest.

■ Lipstick: matt blue-rose, but also pink if it is not too aggressive, gentle violet and fresh melon red. Caution: Summer types easily look too made-up with strongly-coloured lipsticks.

■ Eyeshadow: cool, smokey pastel tones, but also brown if it goes more towards grey instead of red, clear yellow and cool rose. A pearly shine suits the Summer type better than the other types.

■ Eyeliner/kohl: no black, but light and dark grey, cool blue, green and turquoise.

■ Lashes and brows: grey mascara or, if the eyelashes need more definition, black. Careful with coloured mascara – it can easily look too strong with Summer types. For eyebrows, use cool, matt brown tones, but be careful with black.

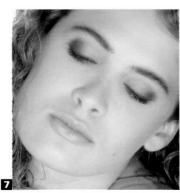

1 *Soft violet and dull rose suit nearly all Summer types and are enhanced by muted rose on lips and cheeks.*

2 *Shiny silvery tones on the lips, the eyelids and the clothes are only suitable for Summer types (and then only in the evening). They are especially beautiful with ash brown hair.*

3 *This Summer type is relatively rare, with more strongly pigmented skin and hazelnut brown eyes. Aubergine and cool red brown suit her best.*

4 *Even a Summer type with fair skin and dark brown hair can look super with aubergine tones — especially with elegantly styled hair and clothes.*

5 *Cool pink, cool blue and shiny ash blonde hair make a decorative trio.*

6 *Harmony in soft, icy tones. So that the whole effect isn't too cool, use red brown with a grey tinge on the lips and lashes.*

7 *For Summer types that tan well: eyeshadow in lilac and cool aquamarine tones, with shiny rose lips.*

8 *Mother-of-pearl rose for nails, lips and eyeshadow — this is a look only for Summer women. Black usually makes Summer types look slightly pale, but it becomes wearable if teamed, as here, with pink and pearl rose accessories.*

AUTUMN TYPE

Personal description: fair skin with golden coloured undertone, either very transparent and with freckles, or an intense peach colour or golden beige. Red hair! If not, then at least a golden shimmer in blonde or brown hair.

Photo left: hair and make-up in characteristic red brown tones. A pronounced golden tone in the hair together with matt red brown lips provide enough contrast and interest. Complementary reddish brown eyeshadow is very subtly applied with lashes and brows in soft brown. Peach coloured blusher and light beige foundation with a hint of salmon complete the picture.

Photo right: also possible – khaki, olive and mustard yellow, petrol and apricot eyeshadows. All red tones that tend towards brown and yellow are right for lips and nails. Only the Autumn type can wear orange and copper tones – pretty in the evening with golden shimmer.

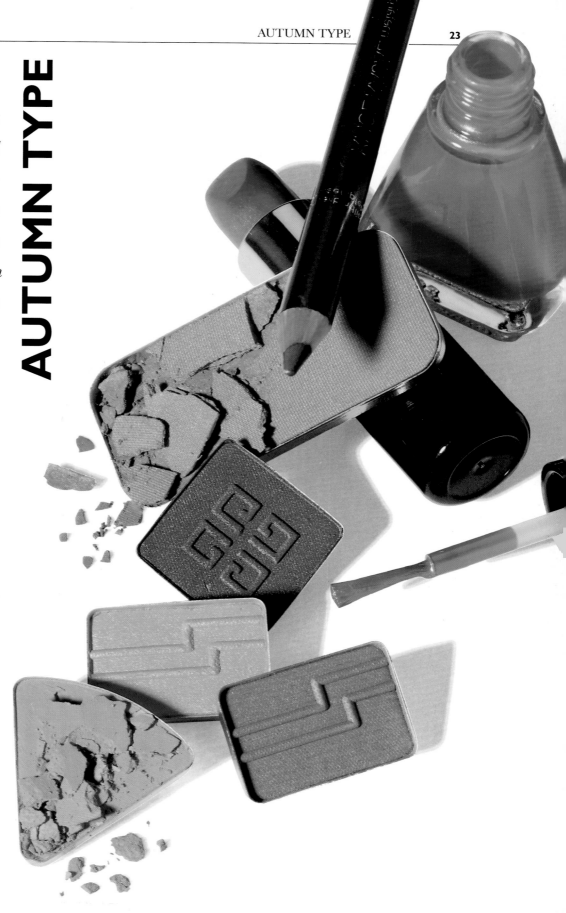

The Autumn type is the easiest of all colour types to identify, with two distinct versions. First, bright red hair and transparent fair skin with golden-brown freckles; and second, super warm beige complexion, without redness or flecks, and blonde or brown hair with red and golden lights (an effect which can easily be intensified with colouring and highlights) Eye colours for both Autumn types are usually very intense. They range from crystal clear blue to petrol, olive to reed green, and to bright amber and brown tones. Autumn types can wear strong, accentuated colours but it is usually best if just the eyes of the lips are emphasised.

■ Foundation: transparent and only warm beige tones only. Freckles should not be covered up with foundation, maybe just with powder (see page 112). During the summer a touch of terracotta powder should be used, as the Autumn type rarely tans. Coloured day cream is also suitable. Even better: self-tanning cream which flatters the complexion's transparency. (However, freckles then look more prominent.)

■ Blusher: on no account use a bluish tone: terracotta powder can look very pretty.

■ Lipstick: warm red, rust, orange or copper. Try rich salmon if a pastel colour is required. No light colours – they make Autumn types look pale. Use a golden shimmer instead of pearl gloss.

■ Eyeshadow: all warm, earthen, dark tones, but applied quite delicately. Rust red, with orange and yolk yellow, blue with a red tinge, and green tones that do not tend towards bluish-turquoise. No icy, shimmering colours.

■ Eyeliner/kohl: brown, warm green, rich blue or lilac; no black.

■ Lashes and brows: brown. Lashes can also be black, with green, blue or lilac mascara at the tips.

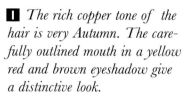

1 *The rich copper tone of the hair is very Autumn. The carefully outlined mouth in a yellow red and brown eyeshadow give a distinctive look.*

2 *An abundance of red blonde curls, a voluptuous red brown mouth, kohl on the lower lid, and dark mascara - with this combination the Autumn type can even wear black (not normally her colour).*

3 *Hazelnut brown hair with red reflections, eyeshadow and lipstick in matching tones. In contrast, a light moss green blouse.*

4 *The transparent Autumn type with freckles covered only with a little powder, reed green eyeshadow and apricot lips.*

5 *Light red hair and very gentle make-up: brown kohl all around the eyes, and rosewood brown on the lips.*

6 *A classical make-up with a lively rust red mouth, brown eyeshadow and a touch of peach on the cheeks.*

7 *With petrol clothes use a lipstick with a grey tinge. The warm combination of the copper red hair, eyeshadow and blusher produces an attractive contrast with the cool colours of the clothes.*

The Autumn type may wear many colours, even rich, bright ones. However, by far the most dominant colour – at least as far as make-up is concerned – is red brown. Contrasting eyeshadows delicately applied show Autumn's clothes off more effectively.

WINTER TYPE

Personal description: 'Snow White' type. Dark hair – from brown to blue-black. Intense, cool iris colours with a clear white to the eye. The skin as pale as porcelain or lightly olive-coloured – in all cases with bluish undertone.

Photo left: black, white, red – the Winter type needs only a few, strongly emphasised colours. Of all the colour types, bright red lipstick suits the Winter type best. Match it with grey eyeshadow and/or a black kohl line, and black mascara on the eyelashes. Foundation should be transparent and just as light as the skin. Only a little blusher!

Photo right: the standard colours for the Winter type: clear red or pink for the lips, cold blue, green or violet for the eyes. However, be careful which combinations are used (see next page).

The Winter type with brown hair and/or an olive coloured complexion is often confused with the Autumn type. If the Winter type wears warm, earthy colours she can easily look boring because these do not suit her. To find out if someone is an Autumn or Winter type it is best to compare complexions. The classical Winter complexion is not salmon coloured; it is rose, and harmonises with all bluish tones.

■ Foundation: light, almost a whitish beige, and thin and transparent, because strongly applied make-up does not suit dark, striking types. Transparent powder, and in the evening an almost white powder, to emphasise the 'Snow White' effect.

■ Rouge: a little. Cool rosy and very lightly applied. No lines should show.

■ Lips: all clear red tones; no yellow red. Also rose with all clear tones from aggressive pink to shiny silvery rose. Violet tones are also suitable.

■ Eyeshadow: smokey grey, grey-brown or light, barely visible icy tones are sufficiently discreet to accentuate the bright red lips. Blue, green and violet in cold, dark tones certainly suit this type, but should be applied thinly and only combined with rose or violet tones (not with bright red).

■ Eyeliner/kohl: black lid and kohl lines suit the winter type better than all other colour types. White kohl on the inside edge of the lid and black between the lashes on the lower lid also look stunning.

■ Lashes and brows: the classic mascara colour is black. Winter types, however, also look good with green, blue and violet mascara with hints of clear, cold tones (but only combined with bluish lipsticks – see above). The brows are usually so dark that they do not need any colouring.

Advantages for Winter types: they can choose dramatic colours and contrasts that can easily look harsh and over made-up on other colour types.

1 *Very pert – bright red, clearly outlined mouth, black framed eyes, and freckles under a delicately powdered complexion.*

2 *Lips, nails and sweater in clear red with a blue tinge, with smokey grey eyeshadow and light complexion.*

3 *Night blue, with violet on the lids - this suits the Winter type if the lipstick is rather discreet.*

4 *Black, white, red - the classic combination for Winter types. Dark red on the lips and a black eyeline on the otherwise unmade-up lids.*

5 *A black eyeline with 'tails', and artificially painted black lashes in the corner of the eye - a cat's eye look that especially suits Winter types. Combined with violet lids and lips.*

6 *Silver eyelids, mother-of-pearl gloss lips, a black eyeline and a flour-white complexion - Winter types can wear this for a change.*

7 *The 'young girl' look: the brown haired Winter type with black-brown kohl and eyeshadow and the mouth in a cool mother-of-pearl rose.*

8 *Exceptions prove the rule: bright lipstick combined with a similarly strong eyeshadow looks attractive because both colours are closely related and the colour of the eyeshadow is reflected in the clothes.*

CHAPTER 2

From foundation to lipstick

- **What is the effect?**
- **What is 'in'?**
- **Tricks when applying**
- **The correct preparations**

BASIC EQUIPMENT

All you need for a perfect foundation

Also recommended: reliable lipstick and eyeshadows, or a second, darker foundation for the summer months

1 *Foundation, to match skin colour perfectly.* **2** *Latex make-up sponges, oval or oblong in shape.* **3** *Loose transparent powder with puff.* **4** *Powder compact (for handbags).* **5** *Powder brush for applying loose powder.* **6** *Blusher.* **7** *Blusher brush (easier to use than the small brushes supplied with the compact).* **8** *Brown powder for shadow (not essential!).* **9** *Tweezers to pluck the eyebrows.* **10** *Eyebrow pencil.* **11** *Spiral brush to shape eyebrows and separate the lashes.* **12** *Eyeshadow powder.* **13** *Eyeshadow applicator with long handle (easier to hold than those with a short handle).* **14** *Eyeliner and mascara.* **15** *Kohl pencil (twist out to sharpen).* **16** *Sharpener for kohl, eyebrow, and lip contour pencil.* **17** *Lip contour pencil.* **18** *Light and dark lipstick.* **19** *Lip gloss.*

FOUNDATION

Foundation covers skin imperfections and gives a nice even complexion. The more make-up you use, the nearer perfection it must be. But always use a light touch.

What is foundation?

■ Foundation (also called foundation make-up or often just make-up) is a skin-coloured cream or liquid which is applied over moisturiser to even out and give life to the appearance of the skin. Depending on whether the skin is to have a natural look or is to appear perfectly even, you can – depending on the occasion – choose between a transparent and a thicker covering.

Why is foundation so important?

■ Foundation is important for concealing skin imperfections such as tiny veins and blemishes; freckles are an attractive exception. If the skin is red and patchy or has a somewhat oily shine, it is difficult to conceal this just with lip and eye make-up.

Ideal for evening make-up: compact foundation from a mirror container. It is applied with a cosmetic sponge and covers the skin perfectly

What kinds of foundation are there?

■ All foundation consists of two components - an emulsion (grease and water) and the colour paste (powder and pigment). In addition there are moisture-releasing and conserving substances and, increasingly, a light protection filter. The higher the powder content, the thicker the foundation covering.

■ Liquid foundation or so-called transparent make-up (usually sold in a tube) is, as the name indicates, relatively runny and contains very little grease or powder. Liquid foundation evens out the complexion, but it cannot eliminate redness or blemishes. Because of the limited amount of grease and powder, it is especially suited to oily skin.

■ Foundation cream (usually sold in bottles or glass containers) is ideal for dry skin as it contains relatively large amounts of oil and moisturising substances. The covering power of a product depends upon its powder content. Basically, foundation creams cover well and are best suited to evening out skin with tiny veins.

■ Compact foundation (usually sold in mirror containers with small sponges) is the foundation with the best covering qualities because it contains the most pigment and powder. Applied with a dry sponge, compact foundation will work almost like a powder but covers better. Normally compact foundation is applied with a moistened sponge, which results in a prettier effect to the face.

■ Make-up sticks are compact foundation sold in a different, elongated form. They have a softer consistency but covering power is the same. As with compact make-up, the colour is applied by using a make-up sponge.

■ Toned day cream, as the name suggests, is a cream rather than a make-up. It protects the skin like a cream and provides a light toning, but does not really provide cover.

How to achieve the perfect foundation

■ The colour of the foundation must match the skin exactly.

■ Foundation should preferably be applied to the skin in small amounts.

■ The easiest way is to put a blob or a drop on the back of the hand and apply it direct to the face with the tips of the fingers.

■ The exception is compact foundation which is not applied with the fingers, but dabbed on with a cosmetic sponge.

■ Preferably apply thinly rather than thickly, and spread in small dabs.

■ Liquid and cream foundation should be dabbed on with a cosmetic sponge so that the foundation blends perfectly with the skin. The make-up sponge should be used with a gentle twisting movement, pressing against the skin.

■ Blend foundation carefully around hairline and neck – make sure it merges well.

How to find the right colour

■ Foundation should be the same basic colour as the skin; the neck should not reveal any colour difference. Only when the colour is neither too light nor too dark, neither rosier nor greyer than the skin colour, will the skin look natural and the foundation spread well without any 'joins'.

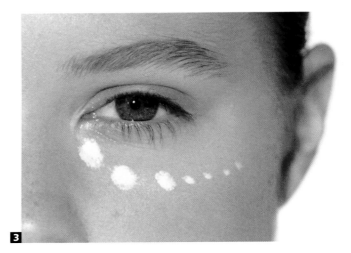

1 *When buying foundation, do not try out the colours on the back of your hand but on an unmade-up face; test the colour again in daylight. The tone that differs least from the skin colour is the correct one.*

2 *Before applying foundation, use a moisturiser – it is better for the skin. The foundation will also spread more easily on top of a thin layer of moisturising cream and will look better and last longer.*

3 *Shadows under the eyes should first have moisturising cream applied. Then several spots of light toned cream should be applied and the colour then lightly dabbed into the skin with the fingertips.*

4 *Professionals cover shadows under the eyes with a fine brush. It is then possible to apply the light toned cream more thinly and evenly to right beneath the eyelashes. Anyone wanting to try this should use just a few tiny dabs of cream and paint inwards to outwards.*

5 *So that the cover colour under the eyes does not become too thick and crease when laughing, the skin should be finally dabbed carefully with a cosmetic sponge.*

As well as the correct choice of colour, remember the importance of the light in which the foundation is to be worn. In warm light, for example, in candlelight and yellow artificial light, the make-up tone can be somewhat cooler – that means rosier colours and those with a touch of grey. Cold neon or daylight, on the other hand, demand warm golden yellow tones. This does not mean, however, that foundation make-up should be yellow brown or red brown. Brownish tones are nearly always wrong, except on occasions when a naturally brown, fresh appearance is required, and the skin tone approximates this colour.

Does make-up damage the skin?

■ Not if you use a foundation that suits your skin type, and the face is cleansed thoroughly at night. The drier the skin, the greasier the foundation should be; in the case of an oily complexion a low-grease product is more suitable. If you remember this rule, then make-up will suit you. Thus the skin is not only better protected from dust and dirt, but depending on the thickness of the colour pigment layer, will also be protected to a certain extent from long-term damage by UV light. This damage can occur as a result of normal daylight, not just through sunburn. The old prejudice that make-up blocks the

pores and prevents the skin from 'breathing' has long been disproved because even the smallest particles of powder and pigment are too large to penetrate the skin. Besides, these days the substances we use do not swell and become heavy on the skin, as was once the case.

Should you use make-up on a blemished skin?

■ Yes – you do not need to do without make-up because you have irritable or blemished skin. Quite the contrary – a good foundation helps to hide blemishes and you feel better groomed and more attractive. However, it is important that the product is medicated, low in

PROFESSIONAL
 TIP *The best light for make-up is daylight without direct sun. The best thing is to sit near a window so that the light falls on the face and not directly on to the mirror. The whole face should be visible in the mirror.*

grease and contains anti-bacterial substances. Foundations for acne or those which are part of skin-care ranges are nearly always almost, or completely free of grease and contain large amounts of disinfecting and infection-preventing substances. If you have spots you should not immediately reach for a special make-up as this can often dry out the skin. Individual spots are best dealt with by using a light spot-covering stick on top of your usual foundation. These sticks contain antiseptic substances that help infections heal more quickly. Tiny blemishes can easily be covered by putting some colour from a spot-covering stick on to a pointed brush and applying it directly and accurately. The brush should, however, be freshly disinfected with alcohol.

PROFESSIONAL TIP *Anyone making up in the bathroom needs white walls, preferably evenly lit. Strip lighting, or a row of electric light bulbs to the right and left of the mirror are good. Light sources from above throw shadows. Coloured walls falsify colours – be careful.*

Shadows under the eyes? How to get rid of them

■ To cover up shadows under the eyes and skin blemishes use special covering creams. These contain larger quantities of covering pigment. The colour should be lighter than the foundation. As an amateur it is better to apply the foundation first and then the covering cream (even though the professionals do it the other way round). It is easier to blend it in with the foundation, and it does not dry out the fine skin under the eyes any more than reversing the procedure. The covering cream should be dabbed on to the skin with a flat brush or a foam sponge, then dabbed into the skin with the fingertips until all the edges have disappeared.

Finally, cover carefully with loose powder.

Should you make up the neck as well?

■ It's best if the colour of the foundation on the face exactly matches the skin tone under the chin. Then it is not necessary to apply make-up to the neck, and there is less danger of producing a line between the face and neck. Simply spread the foundation on to the neck lightly with the fingertips or a cosmetic sponge. Spread to the ears and hairline in the same manner. Then powder the neck. This also has the advantage that tops of blouses or shirts do not come into contact with any colour.

Do make-up products go off?

■ If kept tightly closed and in a dark place, and not in direct light on the bathroom windowsill, foundation should last for about 18 months. If you have opened a tube, a bottle or a jar it is important that as few germs as possible enter. If you take foundation out of the bottle with your fingers, you should first have washed them. If you use a spatula in different foundations in bottles it will only be hygienic if it is thoroughly washed with soap and water after use. Cosmetic sponges that come into contact with the necks of bottles should also be washed often.

1 *A covering stick is the same shape as a lipstick and is more of a paste than compact make-up. Tiny blemishes, spots or little veins on the face, neck or upper chest can be touched up. Covering creams are softer and more suited to larger areas such as red cheeks or shadows around the eyes.*

2 *In order to blur the line between the face and neck after applying foundation you can dab the face again with a moistened and well-squeezed make-up sponge. The colour should blend into the skin colour of the neck without leaving a line.*

3 *Cosmetic sponges must be shaped so they can reach the hollows of the face (crease of the nose, chin hollow and eye sockets). Good sponges are made of latex (natural organic rubber). This material is firm but elastic, and above all has very fine pores. Large pores would soak up too much make-up and not distribute it evenly.*

4 *If your make-up is too shiny just blot the greasy surface with tissues. Press the tissue flat against the skin; do not rub.*

5 *As make-up usually leaves a line where the upper chest meets the neck, it is best not to use make-up on the chest. Just powder it, trying to match the colour with the skin of the face.*

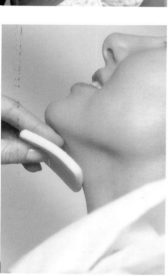

Moisturising or cream foundations, like all cosmetic products, can also be kept for about 18 months. If a product begins to decompose or develops an unpleasant smell, it is better to throw it away.

How to keep your make-up looking good for longer

■ The better the foundation suits the user's skin type, the longer it is likely to remain looking good. If make-up is to last for a particularly long time, for example throughout an evening, here is a trick – moisten the finished make-up with a fine spray of water, dab, and then powder on top. A fine spray can also be applied to freshen the face before making-up.

POWDER

Powder can do much more than just remove the oily shine from the skin. Above all, it is essential as a softener of colours and 'finishes' a complexion

What powder can do

■ There are at least three reasons for using plenty of powder: it removes an oily shine and gives the face a soft, silky shimmer. It fixes the foundation underneath so that it remains intact longer, and – what many do no know – it can correct unsuccessful applications of blusher and eyeshadow.

■ A matt finish: an even, silky complexion is an essential part of perfect make-up; an oily shine to the face demands strong or lively eye make-up, which can look untidy. Only by using powder can a beautiful matt effect be achieved.

■ Fixing: powder is usually applied on top of foundation. By pressing gently into the skin with the powder brush, foundation and powder combine to produce a kind of 'second skin', which not only looks nicer but also lasts longer than foundation alone.

■ Fading: for blusher which is a little too strong or whose edges are too obvious, you only need to dab with powder. The

Loose powder can also be dusted over the face with a thick professional brush instead of a fluffy brush.

colour becomes softer, and the distinction between the blusher and the rest of the make-up is softened. Important: do not wipe, just gently press with the powder brush or lightly dab it on. This is also true of eye make-up: if colours are too glaring or do not blend into each other softly enough, apply some powder with a medium-sized brush.

■ Powder on top of foundation makes the application of blusher and eyeshadow much easier. The brush moves more easily and the colour spreads more evenly. Powder on an otherwise unmade-up complexion gives the skin a touch of perfection. The skin looks better kept, without looking made-up.

■ A pleasant bonus: powder absorbs not only skin oils, but also drops of sweat. It also cools the skin a little.

Loose or pressed: what to use and when

■ Whenever it is possible – and always at home where you usually make up – use fine powder from a large container. Pressed powder in a mirror container

(compact powder) is just for the handbag, for touching up while travelling. The reason: loose powder is taken up easily and in quantity by the skin, it can be spread generously, and if you happen to apply too much it can easily be brushed away. With compact powder, on the other hand, it is only possible to apply tiny portions with a mini-brush; generous application is impossible. Professionals, therefore, only use loose powder.

Rules for perfect application

■ Apply plenty of powder with a large thick bushy powder brush.

■ Do not apply the brush directly to the face; first tap it a little on the back of the hand. By doing so most of the powder will stay on the brush, but the excess with drop off.

■ Press the brush a little at a time against the skin or gently dab it on. In this way the powder it contains will be distributed in sufficient quantity. Important: do not wipe, just dab!

■ Powder the nose, chin and central forehead several times with powder, as these are places where sebaceous and sweat glands are situated. Take especial care to work powder into the folds of the nostrils.

What is powder made of?

■ At one time fine rice or cereal flour was the basis for powder, and from this the prejudice grew that powder damages the skin. The flour became bound with sweat, blocked the pores and caused pimples and blackheads. This cannot happen today. Powder now consists largely of natural talcum, which absorbs sweat and

Before adding powder first remove any oily shine on the skin so that the make-up does not smear. Simply take a tissue that will absorb moisture and press on to the skin – cosmetic tissues, a serviette, toilet paper or whatever is to hand will do.

grease and therefore adheres well. In addition it contains micro-fine kaolin (white aluminium oxide), calcium carbonate (chalk), magnesium powder, colour pigments, silk, care substances and, in some cases, even a UV filter. Compact powder is powder bound with a binding medium and grease. As it can be carried in a handbag, it is suitable for quick repairs.

Coloured or transparent powder?

■ The simplest powder is transparent, that is to say, colourless. It is suitable for every skin and foundation. If you use a toned powder, it must match the colour of the foundation as nearly as possible. If it is applied directly to moisturiser, it should be as light as the skin itself. Be careful with dark powder. It sometimes emphasises little wrinkles and the foundation becomes patchy very easily if the powder is not applied very finely.

Face powder with a gold and silver shimmer is more problematic. It can have a shiny effect that one normally tries to avoid by using powder, especially on the bridge of the nose, chin and forehead. Shiny powder should only be used on those places that can take such emphasis (cheekbones, hollow of the neck, shoulders). During the day it is best to leave it alone.

1 *So that the layer of powder is fine and even it should not be applied too thickly to the brush. Blow lightly across the ends of the hairs of the brush; (a wide brush should be tapped on the back of the hand).*

2 *Brushes that have had a lot of use and are greasy are carriers of bacteria and are unhygienic. In the case of greasy, unclean skin, powder should be applied with a pad of cotton wool that is then thrown away.*

3 *Powder should be applied particularly carefully to the chin, nose and forehead. Here shiny powder should not be applied. Such special-effect powders only look good on the temples, the cheekbones, on a beauty spot and on the arms – and then only in the evening. Pink, lilac, green or yellow orange powders are used by make-up artists for special effects. As an amateur, they are best left alone.*

4 *Containers of loose powder are usually fitted with a sieve that controls the release of the powder. In a compact powder case there is usually a small piece of cellophane between the brush and the powder. It should not be removed as it prevents the brush becoming greasy. If this has already happened the greasy layer can be scrapped off with a razor blade.*

Powder – for blemished skin too?

■ Powder can be used on skin that tends towards impurities and spots. However, instead of using a powder puff that gets dirty easily and becomes a carrier of germs, it is a good idea to use a cotton wool pad. For problem skins there are special grease-free powders with infection-inhibiting additives. It is important to always to keep powder puffs and brushes clean.

■ In time powder puffs not only become dirty and therefore unhygienic, they 'clog' and so no longer take up the powder and disperse it. The same applies to powder brushes. Puffs and brushes should therefore be washed with a mild shampoo once a week. Puffs that become too stiff from washing should always be thrown away; they are cheap and easy to replace. Good powder brushes are made of pony, a weasel-type animal found in Germany, or squirrel hair. They are quite expensive and so should be cleaned with great care. Dab the brush on a hand towel after shampooing and place on one side to dry, so that the air can reach the hair from all sides.

THE EYEBROWS

If eyebrows which grow strongly are well cared for, they give the eyes power and are usually the best shape for the individual's type and face shape

Even eyebrows are subject to fashion

■ In Cleopatra's day thick dark eyebrows were thought to be beautiful. In the 18th century English ladies strengthened their eyebrows with mouse fur. In the 1920s eyebrows were pencil-thin and straight. But since the middle of the eighties they can grow naturally again. So as you can see, eyebrows, too, are subject to fashion. Quite rightly, since besides their biological function of protecting the eyes from dirt and running sweat, they influence the facial appearance tremendously.

What makes the ideal eyebrow shape?

■ Usually the natural shape of the eyebrows suits a person's face perfectly - apart from tiny outgrowths, especially on the bridge of the nose. These tiny hairs should always be removed, because they can make you look gloomy! You can also use a pencil to decide

Dark bushy eyebrows do not need to be brushed. Hair gel or clear mascara will give them shape and shine.

where you need to pluck or colour in (see pages 46 and 47). It is pretty when the tiny hairs at the ends of the eyebrows gradually fade away. A line that falls away too quickly narrows the eyelid and makes the face look sad.

How to pluck properly

■ Plucking is only done where excess hairs grow to the right or left of the ideal brows. If the brows are very wide, they can be plucked narrow, but it is important to remember only to pluck from below, and from inward to outwards. Plucking does not hurt if the skin is stretched tightly between two fingers and in the direction of growth. For anyone who is sensitive and whose skin becomes red, it is best to do this in the evenings. Whether you use semi-automatic tweezers or normal ones rather depends on skill. It is easier to control the pulling power with normal tweezers and the hairs can be gripped with more accuracy. Using automatic tweezers requires practice, but it is

worthwhile when there are large areas to pluck. Whether the tweezers are straight at the front or curved makes no difference, but it is important that they grip well.

Four ways of toning the eyebrows

■ Smooth the eyebrows with a soft eyebrow or kohl pencil. The pencil must have a sharp point and should not be too dark. Do not paint continuous lines, but single hairs, from inside to outside. Finally go over lightly with a small eyebrow brush. Stroke with a pencil the same colour as the brows; this is the best way to fill out holes in the curve of the brows, or to lengthen short brows in a subtle way. Colour in the tiny hair irregularly; this way the eyebrows look much more natural.

■ Fill out with eyelid powder: using a special stiff diagonal brush, powder with gentle grey or brown tones, dabbing between the tiny hairs.

■ Gently brush over with mascara: this brings the brows into shape, gives the tiny hairs a little more colour, and looks very natural. Important: wipe the brush first on a paper tissue.

■ Brush up with gel: ideal to control thick and stubborn brows. There is a special brow gel (clear or coloured) which looks like colourless mascara.

Brow colouring saves time

■ Anyone with light eyebrows who wants to save themselves continually having to colour them, can tone them a little darker with mascara. Professionals, such as hairdressers and beauty therapists, can do it better; the colour they use lasts much longer as the preparations used in salons contain more hydrogen peroxide. In order to avoid harsh contrasts the eyebrow colour should be matched with the hair colour.

PROFESSIONAL TIP *Anyone who has dyed their hair blonde and has dark eyebrows and does not wish to bleach them, can lighten them with a gold colouring pencil. First brush the hairs with the pencil against the direction of growth, then smooth them, and finally carefully brush them back into the direction of growth.*

The colour is applied on the cleansed hairs with a special brush, in the direction of growth. After allowing 10 minutes for the colour to work the cream residues are carefully removed with warm water and a cotton wool ball, without rubbing. Should you want to make the brows lighter (for example, if the hair has been bleached), then use hair bleach, but be careful: you must not get it in your eyes! It is certainly less dangerous to have the task done by a professional.

Does tattooing make sense?

■ In eyebrow tattooing coloured vegetable pigments are embedded in the skin between the tiny hairs. This is an expensive but practical solution if brows are particularly thin or light ; for instance, if the hairs fail to regrow after years of constant plucking. This way you are spared the daily routine of colouring. Tattooing is not recommended for those who are sensitive to pain, as the skin for every tiny 'hair' must be punctured several times, which hurts, even with a local anaesthetic. Tattooing is done using a special piece of equipment - an acupuncture needle wound round with a cotton thread to carry the pigment. Tattooing with vegetable pigment will only last a limited time as the pigment will gradually be absorbed by the skin; usually after about two or three years.

1 *Stretch the skin tightly between two fingers; this eases plucking and makes it less painful.*
2 *Eyebrows that are difficult to shape with lash or brow brushes can be brought under control with a toothbrush. Before shaping put a little spray of hair gel on the brush (not directly on the brows!).*
3 *It is easy to determine whether the brows have the right curve by using two pencils. The brows should begin level with bridge of the nose and the inner corner of the eye. They should end on the connecting line between the nostril and the outer corner of the eye.*
4 *A gentle way of emphasising the eyebrows: powder with eyebrow powder and then paint over them with a special diagonal brush.*
5 *Colourless mascara gives shine and shape to dark, bushy eyebrows.*
6 *Almost finished: mascara is usually enough to give the eyebrows a little more life and tone.*
7 *From left to right: with automatic tweezers thickly-grown areas of the brows can easily be plucked. For plucking individual hairs classical tweezers are best. Stroking the brows with a little gold colouring and a dark eyebrow pencil results in a streaking effect. Eyebrow powder in a gentle chocolate brown can also be used as eyeshadow.*

CONTOURING

Achieving light and dark effects: almost impossible for amateurs, and very difficult for professionals ...

Contouring – what do we mean?

Contouring means using various cosmetic tricks on the face to add or remove features optically. This can be achieved on light-skinned faces, for example, by applying darker powder in appropriate places. The general rule is this: When you want to *reduce* a feature use a darker colour; when you want to *highlight* a feature, use a lighter colour.

Should we contour or not?

■ Anyone attempting contouring should know that it is really only for the professional. Optical modulation can very easily look unnatural if you have not totally mastered the technique, or do not work cleanly enough, and very often daytime make-up is over-emphasised. On the other hand, however, the care

The brown lines and white spots show where shadow should be applied and where it can be lightened. Even beauticians do not always find it easy to acheive the right effect.

required and the large amount of time spent is worthwhile for a special evening. So, what do you need for contouring?

■ By using foundation in extremely light and dark shades, lightening and shadowing can be achieved. The same is true for face powder, which should be either pale or brown. Dark effects can be achieved by using brown blusher or bronze powder. To lighten, special creams are available, but theatre make-up is better value for money, since this can then be mixed (on the back of the hand) with normal foundation. In any case the skin must be evened out with foundation before contouring.

■ Anyone shading with lighter or darker foundation must then make this matt using light or dark powder in the appropriate places.

■ Anyone using light or dark powder to contour must first powder the face generously with a colourless transparent powder.

■ White and brown kohl sticks are good for marking, but making the lines disappear is difficult.

What can you correct?

■ Shadows under the eyes and the inner corner of the eye can be lightened (this makes the eyes look further apart). You can also correct the hollow of the chin (if it is quite prominent), the folds between the nose and the corners of the mouth, and even horizontal wrinkles between the brows, or diagonal folds on the forehead. If whole areas are to be lightened you should use a creamy preparation, and in the case of skin folds, a stick.

■ Shadowing can also be applied to the sides of the nose (if the nose is thought to be too wide), and to the sides of the cheeks to make the face appear narrower. A very flat forehead looks more contoured by shadowing at the sides; the same is true for a double chin or the tip of a nose that is considered too long.

If you intend to both lighten and shadow, apply the light accents first, then the dark. When contouring, it is important to remember to begin with only a little colour and *gradually* intensify it.

BLUSHER

A touch of blusher on the cheeks, forehead and chin livens up the complexion, contours the face and brings a shine to the eyes

A fashion joke – or something to liven up your looks?

■ The use of blusher is subject to fashion to a far greater extent than the use of foundation. Sometimes it is given prominence, at other times its use is 'out'. You should not take these changes in fashion too seriously, but remember that blusher livens up every face and makes it look younger. It also has a harmonising effect; the stronger the eye and lip make-up, the more important it is that the colour between mouth and eyes is matched to give a 'balancing' effect.

Powder blusher or cream blusher?

■ The answer is quite simple: if the complexion has been powdered then powder blusher should be used. If foundation only (or perhaps even just a moisturiser) has been used on the skin, then it is better to use cream blusher. The reason: powder blusher only has a real-

Powder blusher is applied evenly at the level of the cheekbones with a thick brush, and in a way that looks as natural as possible. Stripes of blusher are out!

ly pretty effect when applied evenly to powder; cream blusher is difficult to disperse on powder, and looks patchy on a matt face. In other words: powder blusher is right for complicated make-up; cream blusher is ideal for a more natural make-up.

■ Careful: many blushers contain shiny particles. In the evening their gold or silver shimmer looks good, but in the daylight it looks artificial. Watch out for this when buying, and use a matt blusher during the day.

Also possible: terracotta powder instead of blusher

■ An ideal freshener for a tanned face is terracotta powder (ground clay). It can be used in two ways: first, instead of blusher to achieve a light brown emphasis, and second, instead of moisturiser or toned day cream, if the skin is already brown and you want the brown to be stronger still. In the first case, only using blusher accentuates certain areas (cheekbones, bridge of the nose, temples, chin contour); in the second case, powder is applied thinly over the complete face. In both cases it is important that the powder is

applied sparingly because terracotta is an intense colour and has an unnatural effect if over-applied. Begin with just a little and apply carefully until the desired effect is achieved.

Where is blusher applied?

■ Firstly on the cheeks. Professionals also use blusher on the chin and brows, to enliven the face.

■ Cheeks: do not strive for a particular shape; try to achieve a certain emphasis in the direction of the temples. Even with generously applied make-up, blusher looks best when spread gently and without lines. Obviously visible lines of blusher are a question of taste, but are not currently fashionable.

■ Chin and forehead: a dab of blusher on the tip of the chin and on the forehead give a fresh appearance.

■ Eyes: a little blusher, directly dabbed under the brows, makes the eyes look larger and wide awake.

■ Neck: if the neck is lighter than the face (despite all attempts to match the colour), a little blusher can be applied to balance the tones.

The shape of the face can also be corrected with blusher. You can give more contour to a round face, for example, if blusher is applied in an elongated triangle from the temples, to below the cheekbones, to the corners of the mouth. A very flat, square face loses its angularity if blusher is spread from the cheeks in the direction of the nose. Blusher will make a pointed chin look gently rounded. A forehead that is too wide can be dabbed carefully with a little dark blusher.

PROFESSIONAL TIP *Instead of using powder blusher in the summer, use bronze powder. It gives a pretty natural shimmer, especially on a tanned skin. Important: only put a little powder on the brush and repeat until the required tone of colour is achieved.*

Powder and cream blusher: how are they properly applied?

■ Powder blusher is best applied with a long-handled bushy professional brush rather than a flat, short mini-brush, usually found inside the blusher container. A professional brush is especially suitable for correction; you should only use a broad brush, so that you do not accidentally make the blusher stripy. First stroke the brush a few times over the powder and then knock off the surplus powder on the back of the hand or blow it off the tip of the brush. Place the brush at the highest point of the cheek-bone, and without much pressure move it between the corner of the mouth and the temples. When using blusher it also pays to increase the effect by careful application (as in the case of foundation and eye-shadow); apply it two, three or even four times until the desired effect is achieved. The reason: superfluous blusher is almost impossible to remove without damaging foundation. The colour tone can, on the other hand, be intensified at will.

■ When using cream blusher first take a small portion on the skin and spread it gently. If the cream is particularly coarse, it is easier to apply it with a fine-pored sponge.

■ Blusher is also available in liquid form and as a foam. Both kinds, however, are some-what complicated to apply. Foam and liquid blusher must be quickly spread with the fingers while both are still damp because the coloured liquid dries quickly on the skin and cannot be corrected after-wards.

1 *Which is the correct blush-er to use? In every case, that which best matches your natural skin colour. Blusher colour should always look natural - quite the opposite from lipstick, where extravagant colours can be worn. Anyone who is uncertain should hold up different blusher colours with blue and yellow sticks against the unmade-up face and check which colour harmonises best with their natural skin colour.*

2 *A soft chin contour can be made more striking with blusher and terracotta powder. So that just a light shadow is achieved with no 'stripe' effect, use a bushy blusher or powder brush to apply it.*

3 *The ideal blusher substitute in summer: bronze or ter-racotta powder. It is obtain-able as a fine powder or as hard powder pressed into little balls. The advantage of little balls is that when spreading with the brush very little colour remains after applica-tion, so that it can be applied accurately.*

4 *Cream blusher is dabbed on to the unpowdered skin and spread with the fingers. It has a particularly natural effect, but it does not last as long as powder blusher, and must therefore be corrected two or three times.*

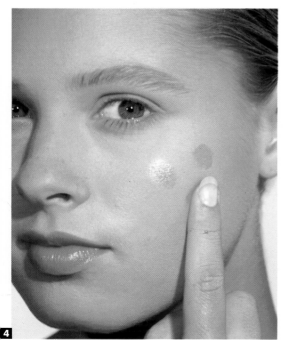

Blusher must harmonise with the colour of the skin

The rule that blusher and lipstick have to match is no longer true, since blusher is less thickly applied these days. The trend is toward naturalness; blusher should look more like a touch of natural colour on the face. The choice of colour is determined by the rosy hue of the complexion. With some people, the blood vessels will show through the skin more than with others. Rule of thumb: all bluish tinges and cool shades rose to pink are suitable for light rosy skin. With skin colour that tends more towards yellow or olive, it is preferable to use warm colours such as apricot, coral, brown or coppers. See page 12.

EYESHADOW

Playing with eye colours is great fun.

But, like every game, it has its rules …

With eyeshadow you must experiment

■ Eyeshadow emphasises the natural shadow effect of the eye sockets and anyone wearing eyeshadow will draw attention to the eyes. The coloured powder is applied after blusher, but before eyeliner, kohl and mascara. Whether you cover the lids completely or partly, apply eyeshadow thinly, thickly, dramatically (dark) or girlishly (light), in several colours or only one, depends on the colour of the clothes you are wearing (and your individual colour type – see page 11), on the occasion and your personal style. But be careful with eyeshadow. Don't use it haphazardly just because it is fashionable. This does not mean that you cannot experiment: quite the contrary. Different colours and methods of application can be tried out to see what is most effective. Quite apart from the fact that experimenting is alot of fun, you learn a lot about make-up.

If you apply eyeshadow very thinly, it can be swept as far as the brows without looking painted.

Powder, cream or stick?

Powder eyeshadow is the most common. It has the largest selection of colours, the newest colour range each season, and innumerable palettes with two or more colours of pressed powder to tempt you to try. The application of powder eyeshadow is relatively problem-free. The colour is applied with a foam applicator or a flat, somewhat broader eyeshadow brush. If you are in a hurry and only a touch of colour is wanted, then even the fingertips will do. Powder eyeshadow is not very suitable for contact lense wearers as powder particles can get into the eye.

■ White, cream-white or lightly rose-coloured eyeshadow is called highlighter (see page 56).

■ Cream eyeshadow is available as a cartridge or in a small container. If the eyeshadow does not need to be applied in a certain shape, the cream shadow may be spread on with the fingertips. As it dries quickly, you have to work quickly, otherwise correction will be difficult. Cream eyeshadow is best for wearers of contact lenses. One disadvantage: it accumulates in the folds of the eyelids faster than the powder.

■ Eyeshadow pencils look like thick colouring pencils and can be powder or cream. With these, broad lines can be drawn and spread out afterwards with a brush, an applicator or the fingertips. Eyeshadow pencils are ideal for use on a journey.

The best tips for application

The eyelid must be free from grease. Any cream remaining should be taken off with a make-up sponge or a tissue.

■ Lightly apply some face powder to the lid with a powder puff or brush (powder remaining in the puff or brush from previous use is often enough).

■ Professionals even out the skin of the eyelid up to the eyebrow with foundation, and powder afterwards. This is especially important with reddened lids. Folds or swellings are, however, accentuated.

■ Do not put too much colour on the lid at once. All surplus is difficult to remove, but it is much easier to increase the intensity without problems. Recommended: lightly wipe the applicator on the back of the hand to remove any excess colour, or dampen the foam head and squeeze it against a tissue; then it only picks up the colour. This is the best way to avoid crumbs falling on to the cheeks.

■ Apply the thickest colour along the edge of the lid. Work from the centre of the eyelid to the outer corner of the eye, increasing the colour intensity as you do so. Then fill in the remaining eyelid with the rest of the colour on the applicator.

PROFESSIONAL TIP *Wash out foam eyeshadow applicators from time to time with soap. Then the powder will stick better and not crumble so quickly. If the applicator is damp the more intensive the colour.*

■ Let the shadow run softly and diagonally up towards the outer corner of the brow, pulling the lid a little towards the corner of the brow.

■ A touch of transparent powder to finish makes eyeshadow more durable.

Contouring tricks for the eyelids

■ There are some principles for shading colour on the eyelids. Here are the most important ones:

■ Inside light, outside dark, with a flowing transition. In this way the outer corner of the eyes is accentuated and the eyes are optically widened. This should not be done if the eyes are by nature already fairly far apart. Otherwise, it suits any eye shape.

■ Below darker, above lighter. Colour apart, the eyeshadow should be darkest along the lid edge and getting lighter towards the brow.

■ Light shadow below the brow optically opens the eye. However, this can easily look unnatural and is most suitable for elaborate evening make-up. It looks better during the day if normal eyeshadow colour is applied extremely thinly below the brow for highlighting.

■ A trick that makes eyes look large: shade the fold of the eyelid dark. The effect is particularly strong if the lid is unmade-up. Brush the colour like an arch, slightly above the fold of the lid, and spread it out towards the top. Be careful, for it can make deep-seated eyes disappear.

■ Small eyes with little room for make-up appear larger if a darker or coloured shadow is applied on the lower lid instead of the upper lid.

■ Eyeshadow on the outer corner of the eye should never run downwards (that looks sad), but always diagonally upwards. Anyone who wants to wear 'cat's eyes' make-up should draw a narrow shadow on the upper and lower lid out from the corner of the eye, and take them diagonally upwards together. Less painstaking: just frame the outer third of the eyelids above and below. This also makes the eyes look beautifully narrow.

1 *Goes with anything, suits everybody: a completely neutral and discreet eyeshadow make-up using smokey grey powder. Apply the colour very gently, and only increase a little towards the outer corner of the eye. With a damp brush, draw a fine line in the same colour along the edge of the lid.*

2 *If the shadow turns out to be too intense, or two colours do not flow softly enough into each other, brush transparent face powder on the lid.*

3 *Powder blusher and eyeshadow colours should match each other and be either in the warmer or cooler colour range. (see also page 12). Here: powder blusher and powder eyeshadow in soft autumn colours*

4 *An eyeshadow palette for use at home: lift all your favourite colours out of their container with a pointed object and stick them on to a pad together.*

5 *A fine layer of face powder used as eyeshadow gives a more transparent effect. If different colours are applied, blending is more easily achieved.*

6 *Special effect for the evening: with dark powder draw a small arch just above the deepest point of the eye socket and lightly spread out to the top. This is especially effective if the rest of the eyelid remains unmade-up.*

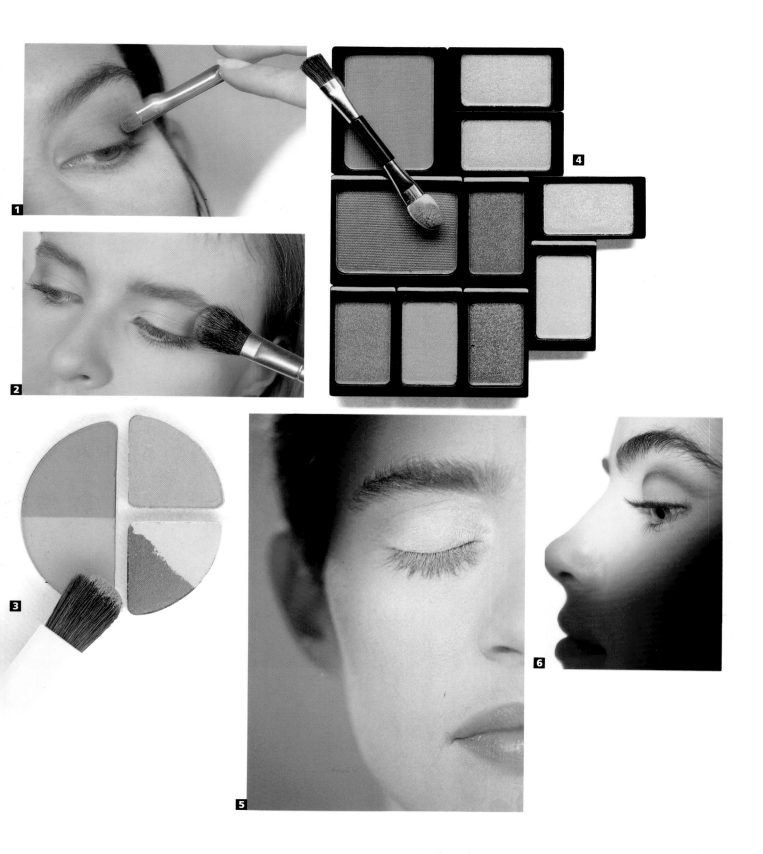

What is eyeshadow made of?

■ The basic ingredients of all eyeshadow are powder (talcum, kaolin), waxes (e.g. beeswax), oils (e.g. silicon and paraffin oils), film medium, binding substances, water, preservatives and colour pigments. In addition, iridescent eyeshadow contains pearl substances.

PROFESSIONAL
TIP

In the evening use eyeshadow with shiny particles. In the day it looks rather artificial. Caution: shine accentuates every wrinkle on lids that are not quite smooth. This applies to gold, silver and copper shades.

Eyeshadow acquired a bad reputation some years ago because it contained traces of heavy metals and caused allergies. Now all pigments are synthetic and are also covered with a fine film of oil, so they do not come into direct contact with the surface of the skin. This has another advantage: eyeshadow can be applied more easily and evenly. As the new pigments repel the grease in the skin, eyeshadow does not settle as fast in the folds of the eyelid.

Eyeshadow colours - how do you find the right ones?

■ The old rule of thumb that eyeshadow should be the same colour as the iris is no longer applicable. The eye colour looks dull if the eyeshadow is the same shade. Complementary colours, however, brighten the eyes. Examples of colour combinations: for blue eyes, use yellowish ochre; for green eyes, use lilac; for brown eyes, use pink. If the iris has coloured spots, make the lids up in the same colour as the dots. The colour nuance should, however, match the colour type. (See page 12).

The rules described above apply even when the lid is shaded with two or three colours. By all means include the colour of the iris in the mixture. Important: when combining colours, ensure that the colours which have a dark effect are placed more towards the outer part of the eye, and the lighter colours towards the inner part.

The colour combinations of eyeshadow are virtually unlimited. It can be great fun to find out what suits you best.

1 *Eyeliner and eyeshadow in matt dove blue.*
2 *Bottle green in light and dark shades - especially pretty with very light skin.*
3 *Completely neutral: anthracite eyeshadow and eyeliner in the same colour.*
4 *Evening make-up: green eyeshadow in an arrowhead-shape with light powder in the middle of the eyelid.*
5 *Extravagant: a combination of pink, orange and delicate yellow. With it an unobtrusive lipstick.*
6 *Suits dark-haired women especially well: rose eyeshadow, muted with some grey. A white line on the lower lid.*
7 *Eyeliner and eyeshadow in light lilac, rose to highlight below the brow.*
8 *Only pretty in the evening, and with completely smooth lids - golden powder. Here it is surrounded by a soft brown eyeliner and a red brown shade on the eye socket.*
9 *Secretive: smokey grey eyeshadow darkening at the sides and softly running upwards.*

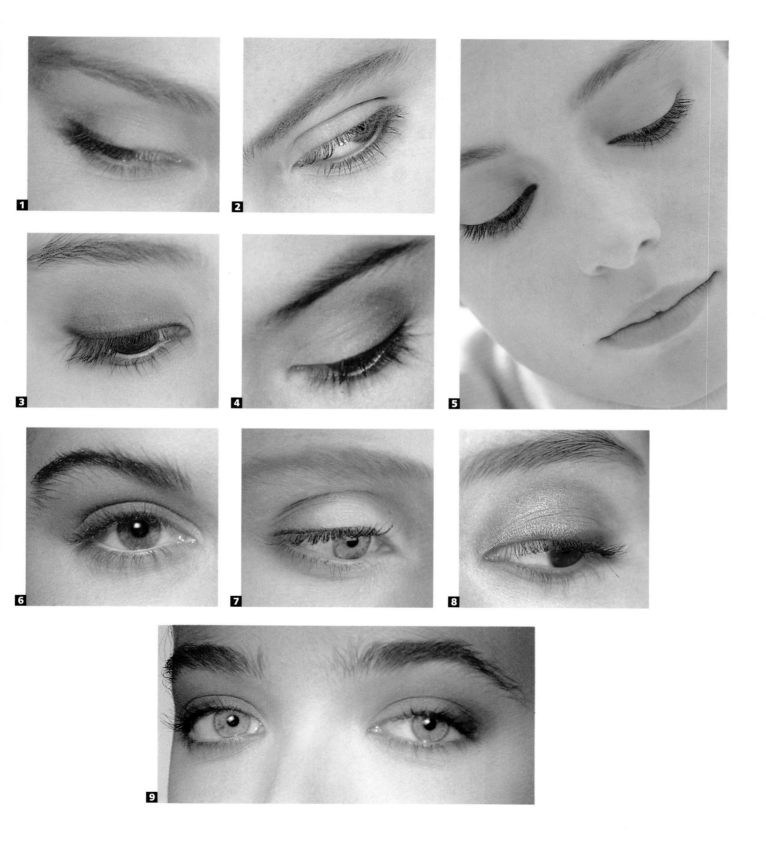

EYELINER

It's not always in fashion but it is in constant use:

the line that draws attention to the eyes

Eyeliner – always relevant

■ Sometimes eyeliner has a little tail as in Marilyn Monrose's days; sometimes it is applied as a thick black line, as it was in the sixties. Sometimes it disappears altogether for years. Time and again, however, it is rediscovered by make-up artists and recommended once more. It is never really completely wrong.

The classic eyeliner à la Hollywood is black and worn without coloured eyeshadow, except in the case of complicated evening make-up. If coloured eyeliner is in fashion (and it is rarely 'out'), then a colour which tones in with the eyeshadow is usually used to strengthen the shadow. Another variation of eyeliner which is always in fashion is a thin, almost invisible line along the baseline of the upper eyelashes. It is a good way of discreetly emphasising the eyes and showing off the lashes to best advantage. The most natural effect is obtained with eyeliner when the pigment of the eyelashes and the brows match.

Applying eyeliner – how is it best done?

■ The classic preparations are liquid eyeliner in small bottles and cake eyeliner, where the colour is mixed with a drop of water. In both cases the liner is brushed on with a finely pointed brush.

■ Easier to use are cartridges that look like mascara and are filled with liquid eyeliner. The brush (as with mascara) is contained in the shaft. Eye pencils that you can use like felt pens are particularly easy to handle: the colour runs automatically to the tip when painted on.

■ Eyeliner applied along the baseline of the upper lashes looks more natural when kohl is used rather than other eyeliners (see page 62).

How to ensure that eyeliner is successful

■ The lid must be as free from oil as possible. If necessary powder the skin lightly, for example, with skin-coloured eyeshadow.

■ Always wipe the brush well. If there is too much colour at the tip, the line will not be fine enough.

■ Either begin the line at the inner corner of the eye and continue it through without stopping, or begin in the middle of the lid and work outwards, filling in the inner part afterwards.

■ Anyone with an unsteady hand should first of all paint on little dots and then join them up a few at a time.

■ It can also be helpful to gently stretch the skin of the upper lid using two fingers.

■ The same goes for a little tail in the corner of the eye; pull the skin gently upwards with the fingers, level with the eyebrows, and then a good upward swing can be achieved.

■ Eyeliner should only be applied along the upper eye lashes after the eyes have been completely made up - i.e. over eyeshadow and after mascara.

Eyeliner as it should be – perfectly painted and its colour matching the eyeshadow and mascara.

A gentler effect: kohl instead of eyeliner

■ Eyeliner is too hard to line the lower edge of the lid: use kohl instead. If you require a softer effect on the upper lid use a kohl pencil here too.

Modern kohl is a colour preparation made into a pencil shape. It no longer has anything to do with the Indian-Arabian 'carbon' made of

---

PROFESSIONAL TIP *Anyone having difficulty applying eyeliner can make little dark dots between the lashes with a well-sharpened kohl pencil. Another possibility: look upwards and paint in the line from below.*

---

grated crystal that was painted on to the lower lid in the days of the 'hippies', giving the eyes a somewhat exotic frame. Today's kohl pencils are either twist pencils with diagonally shaped leads (perfect for the lower lid), or look like an eye-brow pencil and have different hardnesses: soft for the lower lid, harder ones for the upper line. If you are uncertain which pencil to use, test it on the back of the hand; if the lead scratches it is too hard for the eyelid (eye-brow pencils are always too hard to use on the lids).

Tricks when making up with kohl

■ White, light grey and skin-coloured kohl are used for the lower lid. They make the eyes appear larger when applied to the inner edge of the lid.

■ Dark kohl on the lower lid makes the eye look smaller. Kohl gives large, dark eyes more expression.

■ Anyone not able to take the reduction effect on the eyes, but who would still like to give the eyes some contours, should use brown, grey or coloured kohl; after application go along the inner eyelid with a piece of lightly dampened cotton wool. In this way at least some colour will remain between the roots of the eyelashes.

■ A kohl line on the upper lid that is not quite right can be corrected and covered with powder eyeshadow of the same colour. The kohl effect, which emphasises the contours, is therefore retained.

■ If eye make-up is to look completely natural, substitute eyeshadow for kohl. A thin smudged line is all that will be necessary (see also page 79).

■ On the lower lid apply the kohl not quite as far as the inner corner of the eye. The outer corner should be completely ringed.

1 *Extreme eye make-up using a black kohl pencil on the upper and lower lids only suits dark, Mediterranean types. Be careful here: dark lines make the eyes look smaller.*

2 *A black eyeline with a 'tail'. Try it! It does not suit everyone, but can, depending on colour type and occasion, look super.*

3 *White kohl in the inner lower lid makes the eye look larger. The effect is strengthened if a narrow, dark line is painted on the lower lashes beforehand.*

4 *From left to right: a kohl pencil, which can be used to paint a line on the upper lid (see page 61). A twist pencil with a diagonal tip is ideal for a kohl line in the lower lid. Eyeliner pencils must always be sharp and should not be too soft. Practical: the pencil can be twisted out of a cartridge containing liquid eyeliner. Comfortable: eyeliner pencils that function in a similar way to felt-tip pens. Indispensable: cotton wool buds to make small corrections. Dampen slightly before use, so that no bits get into the eye.*

Eyeliner must suit the shape of the eye

■ Eyeliner should follow the shape of the eye and end in the outer corner of the eye. If the eyes are particularly round, it looks prettier to lengthen the line a few millimetres above the corner of the eye. If the eyes slant downwards the line must be taken upwards. If the eyes are close together, the line should start at the middle of the eyes. It should begin thinly, be thicker at the corner of the eyes, and run upwards.

■ Eyelining can be tattooed on just like lip contours. However, this is not recommended. Tattooing needles are extremely painful when applied to the edge of the eyes and as with lips, the procedure can cause injury or infection.

Tattooed eyeliner appears hard and unnatural, especially when the rest of the eye is not made-up, or the tattooing has not been done perfectly.

THE EYELASHES

Mascara must be used. Without pretty painted lashes even a beautifully made-up face will look expressionless

Dark, thick and long, with a beautiful sweep...

■ A lid with long dark lashes gives the eyes a lively expression. Also eyeshadow and eyeliner look best behind carefully coloured eyelashes. Mascara is therefore a must. The layer of colour covers every single lash with a kind of film that does not just tone, but makes the lashes look thicker and longer because even the usually colourless tips are coloured. For blonde women in particular, mascara accentuates their light-coloured eyelashes and brows.

Six tips for applying mascara perfectly

■ The lashes must be clean and dry, because mascara does not adhere well to grease.

■ Mascara brushes must be the correct shape. The best ones have short, thick bristles which form a point at the end.

■ There must not be too much colour on the brush, otherwise

Separating the lashes with a special eyelash brush or comb is easier if the mascara used is fresh and not quite dry.

the lashes will stick together. With good quality products the correct amount of colour will adhere to the brush.

■ Mascara should be fresh. As soon as it begins to crumble, a replacement or new cartridge should be brought.

■ Apply mascara first to the middle lashes; then colour the inner ones.

■ Always work from the roots to the tips of the lashes. Leave the mascara to dry for a little while, then repeat the exercise (perhaps just painting the tips of the outer lashes this time).

Waterproof or not?
Both have advantages and disadvantages

■ Non-waterproof: cream mascara and cake mascara. Cream mascara is made of substances similar in any cream, namely grease and water. Added to these are wax, strengthening resin, colouring and preservative, and more recently keratin (to strengthen the fine lashes) and lanolin to keep the lashes supple. Cake mascara has the same ingredients, only without the water. the dark powder has to be dampened before use.

Non-waterproof mascara is not as hard on the eyelashes as the waterproof variety. The great disadvantage is that you cannot go swimming, and rainfall or tears may cause the colour to run. Advantages: as cream mascara is not water-soluble, cleansing milk or an oil-free lotion is all that is required to remove it.

■ Mascara is made waterproof by adding water-resistant resins. As a rule it will not run when you are swimming or sweating during sport, or if you burst into tears! It also forms a thicker film of colour so the lashes can be made to look a little longer. The disadvantage of waterproof mascara: it dissolves in grease. This means that 'black smudges' can appear under the eyes, so apply a little cream or grease-free eye gel. If you are using waterproof mascara, you can only ensure a clean make-up by using preparations containing grease, e.g. all-purpose cream or theatre make-up. Use a damp pad or a make-up pad dampened with oil to apply them. Sensitive eyes react easily to waterproof mascara.

■ The lashes can be made to appear fuller and longer by the addition of silk or cotton particles to mascara. For anyone wearing contact lenses, however, this is completely taboo, as the tiny particles can easily get under the lenses.

Eyelash colouring: nice for the holidays

☑ In just the same way as the hair or eyebrows can be dyed so, too, can eyelashes. The colour lasts for about four weeks. Dyed eyelashes are practical on holiday if you want to use little or no make-up or if you have light lashes which you do not want to fade into insignificance in the evening once you have taken off your make-up, or at breakfast before you have applied it.

Colouring lashes yourself is not very easy. The dye needs to be applied close to the edges of the lashes, but must not get into your eyes and your eyes must be kept closed as the colour is taking effect. The colourings available for home application are weaker than those used by beauticians and hairdressers, so for all the work involved it is hardly worth the trouble. The best thing to do is to seek the help of a professional.

1 *Eyelash curlers bring a little life to the lashes. Place the tweezers right up close to the edges of the lashes so that you apply the pressure in exactly the right place.*

2 *The easiest way to get at the upper eyelashes is with a brush, while lifting the chin slightly. When applying mascara to the lower lashes, tip the head slightly to one side*

3 *Single lashes, cut from a band: hold with pointed tweezers and position in the right place.*

4 *From left to right: how false eyelashes should be – composed of long and short lashes not too close together, attached to a very thin thread. Using a special glue, they are attached after the application of eyeshadow but before eyeliner, and are glued right behind your own lashes. Check the length of your eyelids to make sure the lashes fit, and do not position them right into the inner corner of the eye. Before removing your eye make-up, gently pull off the false eyelashes, place them on paper and clean them with make-up remover. Practical: a double cartridge – coloured mascara at one end and clear mascara at the other. Indispensable: brushes and combs to separate the lashes. Most important: spiral brushes which twist, often needed under the eyelash roots. Professional: eyelash dye, mixed with peroxide, which colours eyelashes more intensely.*

Permanent eyelashes can withstand (almost) anything

■ Where usual false eyelashes are intended just for occasional evening use and can be easily removed, permanent false eyelashes can last up to five weeks. They are either glued singly or in groups of up to 10 lashes on to the roots of the real ones with a special glue. They are waterproof; you can take a shower and wash your hair while wearing them. You should not get mascara on them, because the grease can make them fall out. You can attach permanent eyelashes yourself, but anyone wanting to be sure that they are properly attached should have the job done by a beautician.

Do eyelashes really need all this extra care?

Eyelashes that have make-up removed properly every night do not need extra care. The traces of oil and moisture left by eye make-up remover or night cream are sufficient to keep the lashes supple. Anyone wishing to take extra care, however, can use colourless mascara. This contains oil, proteins, keratin and other substances to help keep the lashes supple. Those with long, dark eyelashes which don't need any extra colour will find the lustre improves if colourless mascara is used.

What makes eyelashes grow longer?

■ Nothing, unfortunately. How long and thick they are, and how quickly they grow is genetic, and cannot be changed. On the upper lid there are between 90 and 160 lashes, with a minimum length of 8 millimetres to a maximum of 12 millimetres. About 75 to 80 lashes grow on the lower lid, measuring between 6 and 8 millimetres. The life of lashes is only a few months. Normally, one does not notice eyelashes falling out, as by this time replacement hairs have already grown to their full length.

THE LIPS

Painting the lips - easy surely? Can't everyone do it? It's possible, but professionals know a lot of tricks that are worth learning

What the shape of the mouth and lipstick colour reveal

■ There is hardly any other part of the body that sends out as many signals as the mouth. It can entice, sulk or defend. A bad mood shows itself more often than not when the corners of the mouth go down. Certain characteristics are attributed to the shape of the mouth, and equally to the colour a woman chooses for her lipstick – it is said that red reflects a mistress in the art of living, pink the romantic, orange red the extravagant and pearl the successful woman.

The ABC of perfect lip make-up

■ The more obvious the colour of the lipstick, the more accurate its application needs to be. The five most important points:

■ Apply a moisturising preparation to make lips supple and prevent chapping.

■ With the help of a sponge, dab on a few spots of cream, moisturiser or foundation. The lipstick will then spread more evenly and stay on longer.

■ Using a lip contour pencil, draw around the line of the lips exactly. It is best to begin with the 'V' in the centre of the upper lip and work towards the corners. Follow the line on the lower lip from left to right without stopping. Anyone not able to draw the line properly should place tiny dots close to each other.

■ The surface of the lips should then be painted not with a lipstick but with a lip brush. Use a little colour each time and spread it from the centre to the corners of the mouth.

■ To remove excess colour that would otherwise end up on the teeth, press a paper tissue against the lightly open mouth. If the effect of the single layer of colour is still too weak, then make up again. The second application makes the lip colour more intense and durable.

Why is the contour pencil so important?

■ In the first place it gives the lips shape and prevents the lipstick becoming ragged. If the mouth is no longer quite smooth, one should carefully trace the contours of the lips regardless of whether you intend to use lipstick, gloss or a care preparation. The lips can then be smudged with a cotton bud so they do not have a hard line.

■ If you want to make corrections, it is possible to cheat using a contour pencil (more about this on pages 110-111). The contour pencil should be the same colour as the lipstick or at least a shade darker.

Lipstick is not just lipstick

■ Lipsticks are made of oils like avocado, jojoba and rhizine, waxes (lanolin) and colouring (synthetic pigments as a rule). The proportions of these substances determine the characteristics of the lipstick.

■ Cream matt lipsticks have the highest quality of colouring (approximately 10 per cent). They therefore cover and adhere very well.

■ With gloss lipsticks the proportion of colour is 5 to 8 per cent lower, and the proportion of oil that much higher. The effect: gloss and transparency.

■ Lipsticks with a pearl gloss contain synthetic glimmer particles and a lot of lanolin.

Variations of the classic lipstick – gloss creams and lip powder

■ Gloss creams mainly provide shine. This is largely provided by the quantity of lanolin – about 45 per cent. Gloss can be applied as it is or dabbed on as a shiny spot on the lips. Gloss from a bottle is spread on with a finger, gloss from a cartridge with an applicator.

PROFESSIONAL TIP *To obtain a perfect matt finish on the lips, place a layer of tissue on the closed lips and sprinkle generously with transparent powder. The tissue works like a sieve; it only lets enough powder through to fix the colour and make it matt.*

■ Lip powder looks like powder eyeshadow, and is applied with a sponge applicator in just the same way. As lip powder contains hardly any grease, it sticks longer than lipstick, but is not so easy to look after. If you have very dry lips it is better not to use it, or first use a care preparation.

■ A contour pencil contains a compressed lipstick substance with a particularly high proportion of colour. It is as soft as a kohl pencil and can be sharpened with a special sharpener.

How do you select a lipstick colour?

The choice of a lipstick is not just a question of fashion. It should match your colour type (see page 12), and therefore the clothes you wear. In cold light (winter sky, blue neon light) be careful of blue tones, and in warm light (candles, yellow filtered lamplight) take care with orange and brown tones.

The shape of the lips should also influence the choice of colour. Light, glossy colours make the mouth look larger; darker tones make them look smaller.

And something else: teeth which naturally have a slightly yellow appearance will look even more yellow with lipsticks between brown and yellow red. Better to use bluish red tones which are not too dark.

■ Anyone deciding on fairly strong eye make-up should make up the mouth a little more discreetly. On the other hand signal red lips speak for themselves, and as a counterbalance need little eye make-up. An equally strong emphasis of eyes and mouth can appear unnatural.

For perfect application of both lipstick and gloss:

1 *First apply a thin film of foundation.*

2 *Trace the outline of the top lip from the centre to both sides; then trace the contour of the lower lip from the left to the right corner of the mouth.*

3 *Another possibility: make up the lips using only the contour pencil (see also page 49).*

4 *From left to right: typical Spring, Summer, Autumn and Winter colours (for more on this see page 12). It is more important that lipstick matches your colour type than conforms to fashion.*

5 *A lip brush should always be used when the lipstick is to look particularly good and is to last as long as possible. It is easier to follow the predrawn contour lines and to apply an appropriate amount exactly by using a brush.*

6 *Lip gloss: just dab on with a finger.*

7 *Recommended: after brushing your teeth gently massage your lips with your toothbrush. This makes them soft and rosy.*

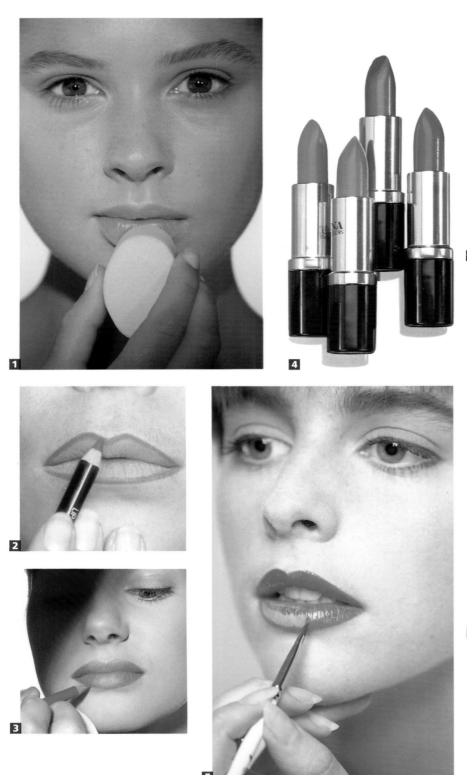

1

2

3

4

5

6

7

How is lipstick made?

■ Oils, powdered colouring and melted wax are mixed together, poured into moulds and, after cooling, fixed into the lipstick holder.

Is it harmful to swallow lipstick?

■ The ingredients conform to the appropriate cosmetic regulations, which allow only tested substances to be used. The colouring eosin, at one time part of all lipsticks, is no longer used because it contains poisonous heavy metals. Oils and waxes used in the manufacture of lipstick have no additives.

A lipstick usually weighs about five grammes. Anyone using a lipstick three times a day and who swallows the colour when eating, will swallow about 16 milligrammes of lipstick. This has no health significance according to the testing authorities.

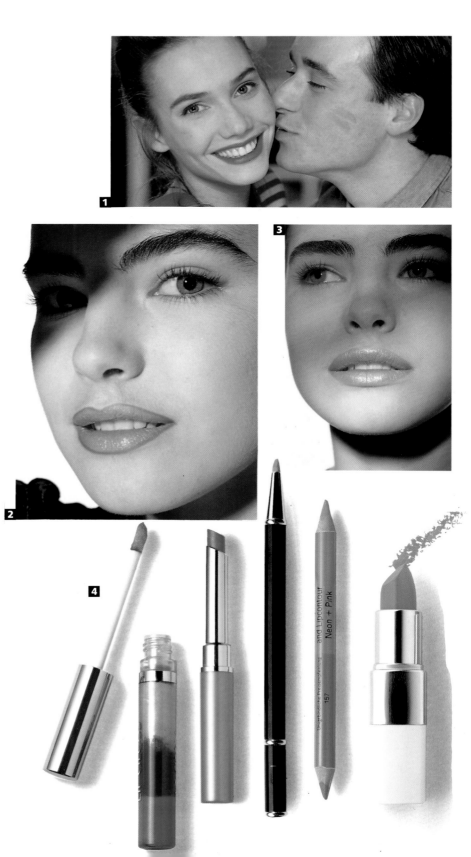

1 *Anyone wishing to avoid leaving remnants of lipstick everywhere (not just on men's cheeks, but also on glasses, cups and serviette!) should use lip pencils, lip powder or matt lipstick, which is dabbed and powdered.*

2 *Lip make-up à la 1960s – for everyone who likes to experiment. Cream the lips, trace the lip contours with a grey-brown eyebrow pencil and spread with a cotton wool bud. Fill out the centre of the lips with lipstick.*

3 *Lip make-up with a strong pearl effect. Only recommended for smooth lips with no wrinkles at the edges, as pearl shine emphasises unevenness; on the other hand a lighter slicked shine gives a smoother appearance. Pearl lipstick looks hard and unnatural against strongly tanned skins.*

4 *From left to right: lip gloss in a cartridge. The different colour levels mix together when you pull out the applicator. A lipstick in a twist container with a diagonal application surface - practical for direct application if you have no lip brush handy. A luxury contour pencil with lead that twists out, and a conventional pencil with a wooden shaft (for use with a special sharpener). The classic lipstick; for the handbag there are mini versions available.*

Does lip tattooing make sense?

■ Make-up artists and some beauticians practice the technique which promises permanent lip outlining and saves daily make-up work

In tattooing vegetable colour-pigments are inserted into the skin and can help where lips have no clear contours. However, the procedure is fairly painful and not cheap. For it to be successful you should only consult an expert as the colour of the tattooed contour and the lips must harmonise so that the unmade-up mouth also looks natural.

What to do about small wrinkles around the mouth

■ These develop in almost everyone over the years, as the mouth is continually moving. One way of preventing these is to consciously relax the face muscles. Once the tiny wrinkles are there, however, there are three possible ways to smooth them. The first is chemical peeling, in which the top layer of skin is removed and the wrinkles disappear. A similar method, with a more intensive effect, is to mechanically sand down the skin. The third method is to treat the wrinkles

with collagen so the skin is filled out from within. None of these methods is without risk, however, and none has a permanent effect. It is important – whichever method is chosen – that you find a specialist doctor to carry it out. As a rule he or she will be a dermatologist.

PROFESSIONAL TIP *Anyone with a round face should not paint on a lip contour that is too striking, just one that makes a clear line. A narrow or severe face, on the other hand, looks more feminine if the mouth is fully made-up and shiny.*

■ Lipstick only looks good on smooth lips. If sun, cold, central heating or sickness makes the lips rough, a few dabs of honey will help, or the application of a protective lip balm. Dry lips should not be moistened with the tongue; this dries them out even more.

Anyone wanting to make up rough lips would be best to use a coloured moisturising agent. Important: lips that tend to dryness should be protected from the sun with light protective preparations, and from cold with plenty of grease.

CHAPTER 3

Super make-up step by step

- Natural make-up
- Evening make-up
- Make-up for work
- Quick make-up

NATURAL MAKE-UP

**Emphasise your
natural beauty**

*Naturalness is desirable –
and with make-up too.
Anyone remaining true to
their 'colour type' should
avoid colours and effects
that are unsuitable for their
face – at least for everyday
make-up. But of course,
once in a while every woman
wants to make an entrance
and to experiment within her
type (see page 60). The
make-up on the left can be
worn by anyone – of what-
ever type or age. It subtly
improves and emphasises
natural beauty; well
maintained skin, sparkling
eyes, and a mouth that likes
laughing (step by step
instructions overleaf).*

1 *Apply moisturising cream to the face and neck. Also cream the eyelids but, if possible, only apply a little to the eyelashes.*

2 *Moisten a cosmetic sponge and press it out on a towel. Put some liquid make-up that matches the colour of your skin exactly in the centre of the sponge. Bend the sponge so that the make-up penetrates the sponge pores. (If the sponge is not moistened the foundation is less transparent).*

3 *Now dab the skin with the sponge, until the whole face is evenly coloured. All the hollows (chin hollow, side of the nose, eye sockets) should be treated carefully. Only apply a little colour, gently smoothing the foundation on to the skin.*

4 *Using the fingertips take a little cream blusher from the jar and dab on to the cheekbones; smooth it diagonally towards the ear.*

5 *Apply some cream blusher on the arch under the brows, sideways on the forehead and on the chin, and smooth in well.*

6 *Where the blusher meets the foundation dab once more with the sponge, as a precaution, so it looks even. Do not wipe, just press the sponge gently against the skin.*

7 *If there is too much shine on the skin, matt the centre of the face (forehead, nose, chin) with some loose transparent powder. To ensure the matt layer remains very thin, a thick brush should be used with only a little powder.*

8 *Line the eyes with a kohl pencil in a neutral colour such as brown or dark grey. Cool colour types are suited to grey; for warm types brown is better (see also page 12). Trace a line from the centre of the upper and lower lid that gets wider on the upper lid. Let the lines come together in the corner of the eye.*

9 *Smudge the kohl line on the upper lid with a sponge applicator.*

10 *Apply black or dark brown mascara, depending on your colour type, making it much darker on the outer lashes than the inner ones.*

11 *For especially natural eyebrow make-up, carefully wipe an eyelash brush on a paper tissue and draw it lightly over the eyebrows, first in the same direction as the growth, then from below to above. Put the colour only on the hairs and not on the skin.*

12 *Apply lipstick that is not too pale but just emphasises the natural lip colour.*

7

8

9

10

11

12

EVENING MAKE-UP

Surprise people with your versatility!

Fashionable but timeless: glamorous make-up for a special event. For women who liked to be noticed once in a while.

1 *The skin moisturised should be finely sprayed; it makes a tired face feel good again.*

2 *Apply foundation. For a dramatic effect the colour can be a shade lighter than that worn during the day. A lighter tone evens out the colour better on the neck and upper chest. Press the make-up on to the skin a little at a time with a dry sponge. Apply lightly to lips and eyelids. Carefully smudge the line between the neck and the ears.*

3 *Cover pimples and spots that show through with foundation or special cream.*

4 *With a powder-puff press transparent powder against the skin a little at a time; be especially careful around the nose.*

5 *Special effect for the eyebrows: emphasise the inner brows; lengthen the outside ones.*

6 *Brush on powder blusher underneath the cheekbones, diagonally towards the back of the head (see page 50).*

7 *If the face is to be contoured (to give it a narrower appearance), brown powder should be applied. So that no join can be seen between the red and brown, the complexion should be smudged with a clean powder brush.*

8 *Also blush the temples, chin, and (depending on the clothes being worn) the neck and upper chest with a brown powder.*

9 *Dab all the contoured areas with some transparent powder to make the colour lighter and softer, and to hide any joins. Powder the neck and upper chest a little before application.*

10 *Eye make-up: put light foundation on the folds of the eyelids.*

11 *Apply dark (grey or brown) eyeshadow first along the upper edge of the lids, then around the outer corners of the eyes and backwards almost up to the inner corners. Be careful: the stronger the accent goes inward, the closer the eyes look together. This also works the other way around: outward emphasis pulls the eyes apart.*

12 *Apply a second colour between the edge of the lid and the fold (night blue is attractive and romantic). Smudge the colours together.*

13 *Lightly shadow the lower lid too. The shadow should become wider towards the outer corner of the eye and allow the upper shadow to go over it.*

14 *Trace a dark line using liquid eyeliner on the edge of the upper eyelid. Whether the line is wide or narrow it must adjust to the shape of the eyelids; on large lids the line can be up to four millimetres wide at the outer corner of the eye. On small lids the line should be narrower and begin from the centre of the lids.*

15 *Using eyelash curlers carefully bend the lashes upwards. Do not place the curlers too low down or they will smudge your make-up. (Bending the lashes upwards before this stage makes the application of eyeliner and eyeshadow more difficult). Finally, apply mascara twice to the upper and lower lashes; black is best.*

16 *Place two or three groups of false eyelashes on the outside of the upper lid, between your own lashes. Dab the lashes with glue and position them with tweezers.*

17 *Using a lip pencil trace the edge of the lips.*

18 *Apply lipstick very carefully; press gently on a tissue and repeat. The lipstick colour and blusher should match and be strong, but not compete with the eye make-up.*

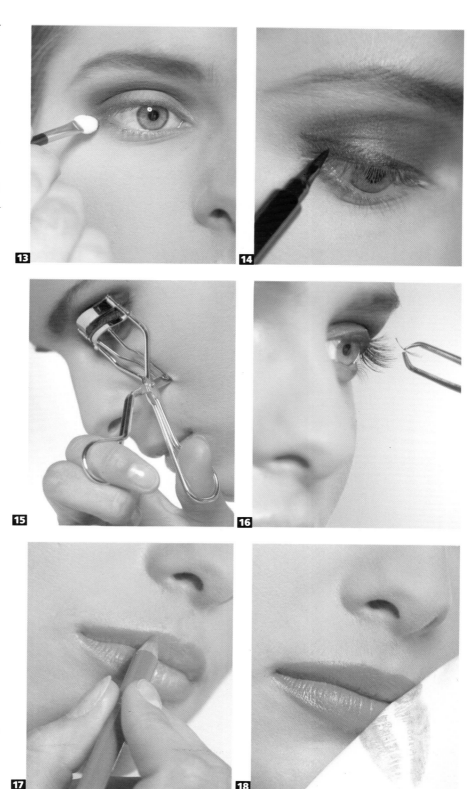

MAKE-UP FOR WORK

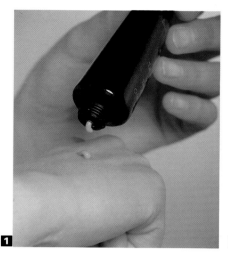

Discreet but assured – the perfect career look

Not to much in the morning, not too little in the evening – fashionable all-purpose make-up for women who exude power and radiance

1 *Even if you're in a rush in the morning, always squeeze foundation onto the back of the hand first.*

2 *Then take off small amounts with your finger tips. Apply to the face in blobs and smooth in. The advantage of this method: the foundation looks very natural, and can be made stronger if necessary, e.g. where the skin is uneven or little red veins did not disappear with the first layer.*

3 *Carefully press the foundation into the skin with a cosmetic sponge.*

4 *Only smooth make-up on the neck to the point where nothing will get on the collar.*

5 *With a large powder-puff take some transparent powder and knock off the surplus on the back of the hand.*

6 *What is left on should be sufficient to matt the foundation.*

7 *Using a sharp eyebrow pencil bring out the natural shape of the brow arch a little. Then gently go over it with a small dry brush. Another possibility: put some hairspray on the brush and use this on the brows.*

8 *Brush powder blusher of a discreet natural tone on the cheekbones in such a way that no lines appear. The blusher should look like a gentle wisp of colour.*

9 *To open the eyes also apply some powder blusher on the eyelids, up to the brows.*

10 *Draw a fine kohl line on the lower lid close to the lashes, and a broader one on the upper lid. Both lines should thicken towards the outer corner of the eye and join there. Do not start at the inner corner of the eye, but in the centre of the lid or the first third of it. Dark grey and dark brown are ideal colours because they are neutral — depending on your colour type (see also page 12).*

11 *Put some eyeshadow of the same colour on the applicator and gently blur this with the lid line.*

12 *Shade into a V-shape, putting a little more eyeshadow on the outer corner of the eye. With dark colours it is especially important that it is used very sparingly, maybe applied several times until the desired effect is reached.*

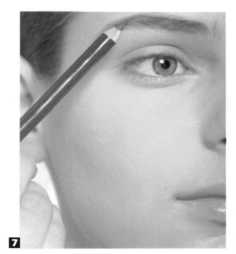

7

8

9

10

11

12

13 *Black mascara on the eyelashes; twice on the top ones and once on the bottom, being especially careful with the outer lashes.*

14 *Lightly rub Vaseline or a similar salve into the lips to soften them; the contour pencil will glide better. Remove excess with a tissue.*

15 *Carefully outline the lips. It is easiest to start in the centre of the upper lip and draw the line towards the corner of the mouth, first on one side and then on the other.*

16 *The outline should not be on the outside of the lips but rather the inside, ending precisely at the edge of the lips (for exceptions, see pages 110 and 111). Precisely drawn lip lines are especially important when the natural ones are uneven in places.*

17 *Paint the lips. If you are in a hurry do this with lipstick; other wise use a lipbrush. Be especially careful at the corners of the mouth.*

18 *Lip make-up lasts a long time if a layer of tissue is lightly pressed against it and some loose powder applied with a brush. However, this takes away the gloss. If gloss is desired, put some more lipstick on afterwards.*

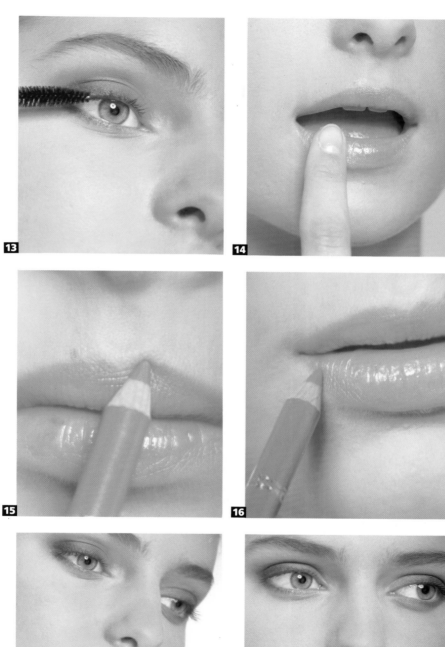

QUICK MAKE-UP

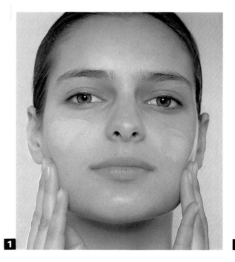

Quick tricks for leisure time and on journeys

A natural and effective look does not require a long time in front of the mirror. And what's more you can get by with just four products!

1 *Instead of both moisturiser and foundation, just use a lightly coloured moisturiser. Alternatively, if you have greasy skin, apply compact foundation like powder – with a dry sponge.*
2 *Frame the outer corner of the eye with a dark kohl pencil.*
3 *Only put mascara on the outer lashes – top and bottom.*
4 *Wipe the mascara brush on a tissue and very lightly go over the brows with it.*
5 *This saves using real blusher: draw two stripes on the cheekbones with a cream lipstick and smooth it in.*
6 *Dab the lips with the same colour – finished!*

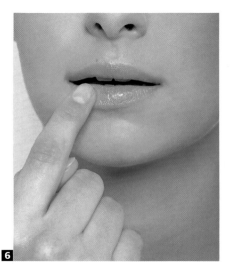

CHAPTER 4

Skin care and protection

- **The A–Z of taking off make-up**
- **Appropriate care for different skin types**
- **Shopping: choosing the right products**
- **Protection from the sun and cold**

SKIN CARE

There is no doubt that make-up helps to make you look pretty. However, foundation, powder and eyeshadow are only effective on skin that is very carefully looked after. This means strict daily cleansing, use of the right products and extra care once in a while.

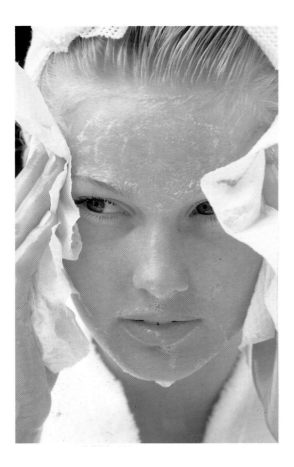

■ The right assessment of skin type is of the utmost importance when choosing care preparations. Only when creams and lotions correspond to the needs of the individual skin and the effect they have is correct, can the desired result be achieved. Anyone who is not sure of their skin type should ask a good beautician for a skin diagnosis, or try to determine their type with the following test. For this you need good light, a mirror and a packet of fine tissue paper (cigarette paper is best of all). This is what you do: wash the skin with a mild soap and do not apply cream. After an hour check the condition of the skin.

■ *Mixed skin* initially tightens and then begins to feel normal again. Press the tissue against the forehead, nose and cheeks. There will be recognisable traces of oil on the tissue from the forehead and nose.

■ *Dry skin* will be tight an hour after washing and there will no traces of grease on the test tissues.

■ With *oily skin* the centre part of the face shines visibly and on all test tissues clear traces of grease will be found.

Care of mixed skin

■ Mixed skin is the most common and is the normal skin type. It can even be an advantage if the middle part of the face is oilier than the rest. Forehead, nose and chin protrude somewhat and therefore need more protection. If the skin there occasionally shines a little, there is no need to apply anti-shine preparations. Skilful handling of powder (see page 41) is nearly always sufficient to keep the problem under control. It is a different picture altogether if the middle part of the face is very oily and tends towards dirtiness, especially during puberty and later. In this case special preparations to combat oily skin can be helpful.
As with all skin types, daily cleansing is vital. Even the best make-up must be removed at night if the skin is to stay beautiful and clear.

■ Cleansing preparations that are washed off with plenty of water are the most suitable for mixed skin because they are thorough yet mild, as well as being refreshing and easy to use. Whether you use cleansing milk which is washed off, a clear wash gel, a wash cream or a non-alkaline wash or soap can be left to your personal preference. All these products are available for normal and mixed skin. Incidentally, the non-alkaline product should not be confused with normal alkaline soap. Normal soap does not remove make-up very well, and also temporarily throws the acid value of the skin out of balance - hardly helpful, especially if the centre part of the face is oily.

Mixed skin with just a small central oily area only needs a thorough wash with a cleansing preparation at night. In the morning it is sufficient to freshen up the face with lukewarm water. With a very oily central area of the face very different care is required: here the preparation should also be applied in the morning. Always important: wash it off with plenty of lukewarm water.

■ It is not necessary to use a proprietary skin toner after using water to remove cleansing preparations. It is worthwhile buying it, however, if the centre of the face is very oily. A lotion containing some alcohol and herb extracts to contract the pores is ideal. Put it on the nose, forehead and chin, morning and night. This helps to combat the oily shine and gives the skin a finer appearance for a while.

■ Creams and emulsions (milk) for the mixed skin contain plenty of moisture but too much oil. Preparations for normal skin usually contain the right balance. For young skin a single milk or cream for day and night use is sufficient. Should the skin in the central part of the face become oilier, which can happen just before and during menstruation, or in the summer, these areas should simply be excluded from treatment.

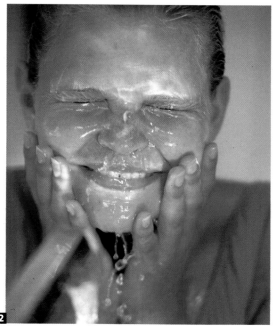

1 *When taking off eye make-up avoid stretching the skin. It is best to use a special remover or pad that loosens mascara easily.*
2 *Apply a wash cream or lotion, and wash off thoroughly with plenty of lukewarm water. Residues are harmful to the skin.*
3 *Never rub the face; just gently dab it dry.*

1

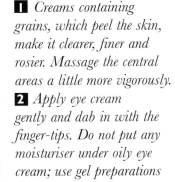

2

1 *Creams containing grains, which peel the skin, make it clearer, finer and rosier. Massage the central areas a little more vigorously.*
2 *Apply eye cream gently and dab in with the finger-tips. Do not put any moisturiser under oily eye cream; use gel preparations in addition to day cream.*

■ Useful extras: rubbing the skin with a preparation containing small grains refines the skin's appearance, because the grains remove dead skin cells from the surface and so prevent hardened skin. This is especially good for the central area of the face. Apply the preparation instead of the usual cleansing product two or three times a week. massage the oilier areas more rigorously, and the areas on the sides a little more softly.

■ Moisturising masks are very helpful if the sides of the face become drier than usual (e.g. in the winter because of hot air from heating). After exfoliating the skin with a preparation containing small grains, cover the central part of the face with the moisturising mask. (Leave this area untreated if it is very oily. If necessary apply a mask for greasy skin here).

Care of dry skin

■ Skin looks as its most beautiful when young and well maintained – soft with a rosy hue and fine pores. There is no problem with blackheads and spots. Unfortunately, dry skin is also very sensitive producing very little in the way of protective substances to combat harmful elements in the environment and prevent loss of moisture. Uncomfortable tightness, itching and scaly skin can result. Dry skin therefore tends towards fine wrinkles earlier than other types.

However, modern cosmetics have made it possible to make up the deficiencies of dry skin. Despite this, however, the rule for taking care of dry skin must be little is sufficient. This tender skin does not like being neglected, but also reacts sensitively to over-treatment or a continual change of care products. A modest, well thought-out programme consistently applied is best for dry skin.

■ For cleansing, milk containing oils – from a range of products for dry skin – is best. Apply with tissues or water depending on the instructions. Even the mildest cleansing will deprive the skin of some of its natural protective substances. Therefore, the milk should only be used at night. In the morning it should be sufficient to wash the skin in lukewarm water, or use a mild toner suited to the skin type.

■ It is a good idea to apply a gentle toner after cleansing with a greasy cleansing milk. The toner contains no alcohol, but livens up and freshens the face. In addition, lotions for dry skin are enriched with herb extracts and moisturisers, and are a care plus.

■ Creams for dry skin must contain besides moisture, a fairly large proportion of oil. Fear of a ugly shine is unfounded: these days the cosmetics industry can incorporate oil into extremely light emulsions that are quickly absorbed. This is different to the care required for mixed skin; with dry skin the purchase of a special day cream is recommended. In almost every case good preparations of this kind contain a UV filter that protects dry, sensitive skin from premature ageing.

■ Worthwhile extras: use eye cream when the first wrinkles appear. A light gel preparation is ideal during the day. Apply it before your day cream moisturiser; this also provides a good basis for make-up.

Cream masks make dried-out skin look supple again, and soften it when red patches and irritation cause problems. Special products for sensitive skin contain soothing vegetable substances like camomile and marigold, as well as healing panthenol.

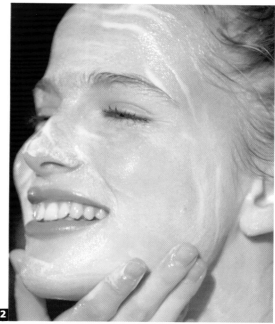

1 *It is always best to dab creams on sparingly. Any shine remaining on the skin after 10 minutes means you used too much. Next time use less.*
2 *Creamy moisturising masks can be applied generously. They help skin to become pliable again and to feel comfortable. While the mask is being absorbed, relax if possible. Then the effect will be even greater.*

1

2

1 *You will be doing something good for tender, sensitive skin if from time to time you apply a fine, vitamin-rich oil. This relaxes, soothes and gives the skin a beautiful soft touch.* **2** *Do something about wrinkles around the eyes as early as possible. Practical: a care preparation in a lipstick format for travelling. It protects the skin and makes it smooth.*

Care of oily skin

■ The best thing about oily skin is that it is more protected from environmental influences and premature ageing because it produces its own protective film. This, however, becomes a problem when the layer begins to shine on the surface of the skin. Together with dead cells, it blocks the pores.

Consistent care of greasy skin can give it a clear appearance. In particular, it can prevent the pores becoming blocked too quickly which causes blackheads to develop, which then turn into spots. What you cannot expect from careful attention is a fundamental change of skin type. Oily skin is predisposed to problems, and does not change in any real sense until after middle age.

■ Cleansing is the most important thing for oily skins, and needs to be done fastidiously. The best products to use are non-alkaline preparations. These are liquid washing lotions or firm, soap-type washing substances, containing alkaline-free cleansing substances. They degrease the skin more thoroughly than cleansing milk, and do not alter – as soap will – the skin's natural pH value. As oily skins are also active at night, you should cleanse the skin thoroughly each morning.

■ A good toner does oily skin a lot of good. It freshens, refines the surface of the skin for hours, and above all prevents shine showing through too quickly. Besides a proportion of alcohol, a lotion to combat oily skin should also contain additives to close pores and antiseptic to resist infections.

■ Creams are only required sparingly on oily skins. The best thing to use is a thin liquid emulsion with moisture and possibly a little oil, or a completely fat-free gel. As the oil content is only specified on a few products, take care when buying preparations, and only buy those that are expressly made for oil skin. This is important so as to avoid greasy substances that encourage the build-up of blackheads. With special preparations you can be fairly certain that they are free of such substances.

■ Worthwhile extras: preparations containing grains, which peel the skin, are a good idea for greasy skin. These stimulate the blood circulation and loosen any hard skin, so that the skin appears clearer and softer. This should be done two or three times a week instead of normal cleansing.

■ Cleansing masks have a similar effect to peeling preparations and also tone the skin. Many cleansing masks contain soothing substances that help infections to heal more quickly. A cleansing mask is recommended as a preparation for make-up that needs to be particularly beautiful and long-lasting.

■ Eye cream makes sense when the first fine lines begin to show, as the skin on the eyelids of an otherwise greasy skin is always dry and therefore unprotected.

Care of blemished skin

■ Acne is a major skin problem that can appear at the onset of puberty, and usually disappears without a trace on its own. However, you should take appropriate care. For example, have blackheads removed regularly by a professional who will also open and disinfect pimples.

■ What you can do yourself: cleanse thoroughly every day with an alkaline-free washing preparation. Do not overdo this, however. Acne is not a question of cleanliness as is often thought. It has hormonal causes that cannot be removed by washing. Rough cleaning will only make the skin more sensitive. Use moisturising preparations for skin care; usually the same will serve for both night and day.

1 Face brushes for massaging with a cleansing lather ensure that closed pores are really clean and are ideal for pale skin with poor circulation. If you cleanse your skin intensively like this every day, you can save yourself having to exfoliate the skin once a week.

2 Steam baths open the pores and soften hard skin. Very useful when blackheads are to be removed, or you want to peel the skin.

1 *Remove blackheads with clean fingers and short nails. It is best to put a little cotton wool or tissue around the fingers, tighten the skin around the blackheads and then press lightly. Finally, disinfect with an antiseptic toner containing 70 per cent alcohol.*
2 *A cleansing mask containing soothing and anti-bacterial additives applied after blackhead treatment prevents infection and makes red patches disappear.*

Special sticks to use on spots and pimples help to get rid of any infection. You should always have one to hand and use it as soon as the first signs of a new pimple appear. You can carefully squeeze out blackheads yourself as these have an open end. This does not mean squeezing areas of your face every time you look in the mirror! Such 'operations' are best restricted to once a week. The skin should be thoroughly cleansed beforehand. Open the pores by having a steam bath or using hot compresses; blackheads are then more easily pressed out.

■ What is best left to beauticians? Fatty cysts – lumps under the skin – must be removed with a special instrument, and this can only be done by a fully-trained beautician. If you try to remove one yourself there is always the danger that an infection will occur and leave a scar. Opening up pimples is also best left to a professional, for the same reason.

■ When is a doctor needed? If you always have more than three or four fully developed pimples, treatment by a doctor is recommended, especially when the pimples lead to reddened, painful knots. With special antibiotics and peeling agents only available on prescription, the excess fat and hard skin can be removed, making acne something that can be successfully dealt with today. The important thing is consistency and persistence in the use of preparations and medicines.

Care of more mature skin

■ Some time from the early thirties the skin will need far more care and attention. Elasticity and firmness decrease, the first wrinkles appear and a poor life-style – too little sleep, too much stress, continually having one drink too many – will have left its mark. Use of preparations with an intensive effect cannot remove these physical marks, but can certainly reduce them, especially if at the same time there is a change of life-style.

■ Ampoule treatments contain soothing substances in a concentrated form. They increase the blood circulation and the supply of oxygen, stimulate the metabolism and supply regenerative substances to the skin. Ampoules are best used as a complete treatment over eight to 10 days. This is recommended when the skin looks more tired than usual.

■ Day creams with a UV filter should be used by anyone over 30 to halt ageing of the skin caused by UV rays.

■ Highly effective moisturising creams are ideal for a demanding skin. They make sure that the upper layers of skin remain smooth and elastic. Especially good are preparations containing fatty acids and substances that strengthen the links between cells, providing better moisture retention and making the skin more resistant to everyday wear and tear.

■ Vitamins can help the skin to remain young much longer – even when applied externally. This is particularly true of vitamins A, E and C. They can render harmless aggressive molecules, which today are considered the factors mainly responsible for early ageing of skin. These 'free radicals' attach themselves to healthy cells, weakening and damaging them.

■ Masks which tighten the skin are unbeatable when it comes to making traces of tiredness invisible - at least for a certain period of time.

■ Most important of all: from now on you must take daily care more seriously. Sometimes this takes real effort, as spectacular results are rarely possible over a short period. You will only discover in succeeding years, with a skin that has remained youthful, that the effort pays off and continues to be effective.

1 *Ampoule treatment supplies the skin with concentrated substances that encourage and improve the metabolism.*
2 *The neck is one of the skin's 'dry zones'. Especially rich treatment here does a great deal of good*
3 *Gel masks will quickly make you look pretty. They are refreshing, and enliven and smooth the skin for hours – even if it has fine wrinkles.*

Finding the right products for you is not always easy since you will find competent, individual advice everywhere cosmetics are sold. However, bad buys can be avoided. Heed a few rules and you have a good chance of getting what is right for you.

WHAT TO BUY

■ Important: when seeking advice do not wear make-up and powder. If possible do not even put on cream. This will make the diagnosis of your skin type easier – the most important thing to be decided when trying to establish the skin care suitable for you. Recognising skin types demands expert knowledge and some experience, and both are not always available. So make things easy for your adviser.

■ Before buying any products write down which cosmetics have been good for you in the past, and which have not. The more precise you can be in the shop the better your chance will be of bringing the right products home.

■ You should consider beforehand what you can expect from new products. Don't forget: today cosmetics can do a great deal – but they still cannot work miracles. For example, there is no substitute for a healthy way of life. The formation of wrinkles can be delayed a little; those already formed can only be reduced. Care can get a skin type into good condition - but it cannot fundamentally change it. You cannot expect more, and more should not be promised.

■ You must state clearly if you have an allergy, even if not a cosmetic allergy – for example, hay fever. A well-informed sales assistant should be able to recommend a suitable, well-tried course of treatment for anyone with allergies; some of these products are known as hypo-allergenic. They offer a relatively high guarantee of tolerance.

It's difficult to decide which is the right cosmetic. Professionals say the important thing is not the image of the cosmetics company or the price of the product, but the condition of the skin after two to three weeks thorough use of the product.

■ When trying newly recommended products only buy the smallest size at first. This will be relatively more expensive, but if you do not use all the larger size because the preparation is not suitable for your skin, you will end up paying more. When buying more, check the price of jars verses tubes. Often the price of a tube is better value for money.

How can you recognise good advice?

■ A competent, enthusiastic advisor will first of all check your skin. You will know that you are in goods hands if your skin condition is also checked when you buy the product next, since things can change with time. It is a bad sign if the sales assistant pays little attention to your skin and immediately reaches for the product on the shelf. In this case it is best to walk away.

■ A good advisor will make enquiries about a customer's personal experience with cosmetics. It is a bad sign if the sales assistant attempts to convince the customer that she has no idea what does and does not suit her skin well. Everyone knows how their own skin reacts.

■ The ideal advisor is a likeable person. In the end advice is a question of trust, and trust presupposes sympathy. If there is no point of contact with an assistant, it is best to break off the discussion.

■ A sympathetic assistant will also show understanding of financial restraints. It is a good idea to state right at the outset how much you spend on cosmetics each month. It is a bad sign if you end up spending your whole budget on just one expensive cream.

COSMETICS TERMINOLOGY

Exfoliation: *the peeling of hard skin from the surface of the complexion. It is a natural process, which can be encouraged by cosmetic peeling.*

Collagen: *the material from which the connective tissue is made, which is responsible for the skin's moisture layer. Specially prepared collagen in cosmetics should preserve the moisture in the upper skin layers.*

Lip-proteins: *micro-capsules in emulsions and gels which serve as a transport medium, bringing the active substances into the skin.*

Natural moisturising factor: *natural substances and laboratory-made substances which imitate nature, which take up and bind water..*

Cosmetic peeling: *use of creams, washes or cleansing masks containing small grains of vegetable enzymes, to remove hardened skin cells.*

Regeneration: *the renewal of the upper skin, by which new cells are continually formed to replace and extend worn hard skin.*

pH or acid value: *the unit of measurement which gives the chemical acidity of the skin. With healthy skin it lies between pH 5.3 and 5.8*

Alkaline-free cleansing substances: *liquid washes, lotions or soap-type substances. Often better to use than ordinary soap.*

EXTRA TIPS

Sun, cold and stress can damage the skin and special care can help to counter some of these effects. However, prevention is better. A lot of damage is not seen immediately, only later when it is almost impossible to improve matters.

Skin protection against the sun

■ Sun is a treat for the body and soul. But only in small quantities. Even a little too much is unhealthy, particularly for the skin. The free radicals already referred to (page 99) are to blame for this; they arise as a result of UV sunlight on the skin. These molecules destroy healthy cells, lead to sunburn and diseased changes in the skin, and the tissues grow old prematurely. This can be avoided by following these rules:

■ Never go out in the sun without sun shield. Its cosmetic UV filters break up the energy from UV rays, especially on the surface of the skin, and prevent damage to the skin's cells.

■ With sensitive skin never use less than protection factor 10 to start with. Theoretically you can then stay out 10 times longer in the sun with this protection than without, before reaching the damaging dose. However, do not go to the limit of this protection, as sensitivity to the sun and its strength cannot be estimated exactly.

■ And remember, cream yourself again regularly, since sweating causes the protective film to become transparent before the allowed exposure time expires.

■ Keep out of the sun altogether when the factor protection time has expired. Even adding extra cream will no longer prevent you from getting burned then.

■ Avoid the midday sun at all costs. The hot infrared rays of sunlight considerably strengthen the damaging effect of the UV rays.

■ Use the morning sun to tan as often as you can. The sun's rays are relatively gentle until approximately 10 am.

Nothing can age the skin more than lying in the sun too long. And never lie with your face in the sun without protecting your eyes.

■ For after-sun care use light emulsions and gels containing plenty of moisture. Products rich in oils increase the amount of heat in the tissues instead of reducing it.

■ Tip: if the skin has slightly reddened, use a self-tan the produce a nice colour. Careful: do not let the artificial tan deceive you into thinking that the skin can take a little more sun for a few days.

Skin protection against the cold

■ Sharp winds and winter sub-zero temperatures are especially difficult for dry skins, because of the small amount of moisture in the air when temperatures are low. Also bad: indoor and outdoor contrasts in temperature which cause the skin to lose more of its own protective substances than it can replace. The result: stretching, burning, redness and flaking. Where there is a tendency to weak connective tissue, strong red veins form. The best preventative measure against such damage is to use holistic cosmetics, i.e. those which do not just concern themselves with the face.

■ Hot and cold showers, which you should begin taking in the autumn, help to improve your overall circulation. The skin's tiny blood vessels will then be better prepared for sudden temperature changes. The better your blood circulation, the fewer problems you will have with the metabolism and care of your skin.

■ You should be careful about drinking alcohol to warm you up. Alcohol removes excess moisture from the tissues.

The feeling of fresh air on the skin is one of the best beauty treatments. In sub-zero temperatures, the face should be protected with a greasy cream. This will prevent damage to the skin when it is exposed to low temperatures. Warm clothing and vigorous movement ensure good circulation and thus prevent skin damage.

Steam baths and saunas are stress beaters and provide intensive relaxation. Important: afterwards generously cream the face and body. After a sauna the skin is particularly receptive to grease, moisture and cosmetic substances.

■ Cream is more important than moisturisers on a cold winter's day. It works like a warm covering and keeps the moisture level stable. Lips and eyes should be particularly carefully creamed, as the skin here is very tender and therefore vulnerable.

■ Compresses of lukewarm camomile or lime blossom tea will relieve irritation. Boil two teaspoons with $1/4$ litre of boiling water and leave to stand for 10 minutes.

■ Cream masks will quickly make rough skin pliable again. Most of them contain oils and soothing herb extracts, which will alleviate reddened skin. These masks can be used daily, as required.

■ You should only use ampoule treatments in winter if they contain moisture or oil concentrates. Toning and regenerative treatments should be done at times of the year which are less demanding on the skin.

A short anti-stress programme

■ Even really well-executed make-up does not work properly if the eyes are tired and the lines of the face are tense. If (with sensitive skin) wrinkles appear quickly, or (with oily skin) pimples increase, it is not always a good idea to grab your make-up. Instead try to relax quite consciously. This art can be learned and brings many benefits.

■ Massage is a stroking remedy for the skin and the soul. It removes the tension from the fine muscle threads in the tissues, and helps you to relax. Daily creaming should therefore be combined with some massage. Some of these techniques are suitable for relaxing during the day.

– Begin with a head massage. This is good for hair growth and will relax the face muscles at the same time. All 10 fingertips should be placed on the scalp and moved gently in a circular motion. Begin with the temples, go to the centre of the head and massage along the back of the head. This can also be done during the day as long as it does not disturb your hair-do too much!

– After creaming the face, tap gently on the top of the head with the fingers. This stimulates blood circulation.

– To combat lines on the forehead try this: using the fingers of both hands push the skin of the forehead together. Gradually massage back to and away from the temples.

– This will relax the lines of the face: with the middle fingers go along the sides of the nose and the corners of the mouth. When moving upwards use gentle pressure.

– With the middle finger make tiny circles around the mouth. This loosens the muscles and relaxes the lips.

■ Isometric exercises will relax muscles dramatically and help dispel tiredness.

– Place the flat of the hand against the forehead and lift up against the resistance of the forehead. Hold the tension for six seconds, releasing suddenly.

– Close the eyelids tightly, without screwing up the eyes. Hold the tension here too for a few seconds, releasing suddenly.

– Press the lips (not the teeth) together as tightly as possible, and then relax.

Quick pick-me-ups

■ Warm lavender compresses are very relaxing: put 10 drops of lavender oil in a litre of hot water, soak a small, rolled-up hand towel in it, and place the roll in the nape of the neck.

Ideal when you are tired: fill a bowl with cold water and dip the whole face in it. Open and close the eyes a few times under water.

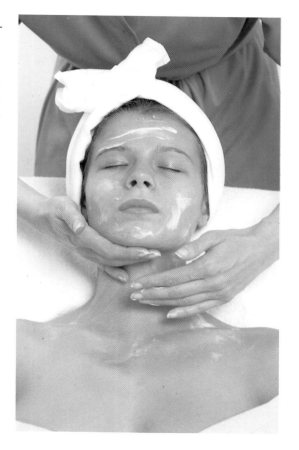

This is something you should occasionally treat yourself to: the luxury of a professional cosmetic treatment. It will do your skin good to be cosseted by trained hands, massaged and spoiled, especially at hectic times in your life. Good beauticians make their place of work somewhere you can really relax and have a rest — without being disturbed by music or chatter.

Tricks for solving problems

- **Hidden eyelids or small eyes**

- **Full lips**

- **Freckles or pale skin**

- **Make-up with glasses**

- **Shape of the face and hair style**

HIDDEN EYELIDS

Never frame the eye!

The only places where hidden eyelids can have shadow applied is under the eyebrows and on the lower lid, because the upper lid usually disappears entirely into the socket.

Definitely wrong: black lines (above). They emphasise the arch over the eye sockets and make the eyes look smaller.

1 *Coloured eyeshadow, applied narrowly like an eyeline, will not smudge if the lid disappears into the eye socket when the eye is open. Very flattering: white kohl on the lower lid.*

2 *Carefully but lightly shadow the area between the lid fold and the brow.*

3 *Shadow applied under the brows and shadow to the side of the lower lid, if possible in another colour, is a good balance. Apply plenty of mascara to the eyelashes.*

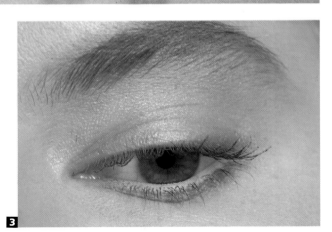

SMALL EYES

Even the brows play a part

For small eyes: painted black lines and compact colour have the effect of making the eyes look even smaller. Eyebrows, which 'frame' the eyes, can be raised by plucking.

1 *Good for small eyes: apply eyeshadow generously right around the eyes. For the most natural effect use a soft brown tone that is not too different from the skin colour. Also good for small eyes: a white kohl line on the lower lid.*

2 *So the shadow is as soft as possible, powder the lids generously beforehand.*

3 *Tricks with eyelash curlers: a nice sweep of the eyelashes is an additional eye-opener.*

4 *Do not paint the eyebrows too darkly and only emphasise them at the outer edge. Feathery hair growing downwards should be removed.*

THIN LIPS

Do everything to make the mouth look larger

It's not a disadvantage to have thin lips. Sometimes they're just part of an individual's type. However, it's worth knowing the beauty tricks which can make thin lips look fuller without them being over made-up and looking artificial.

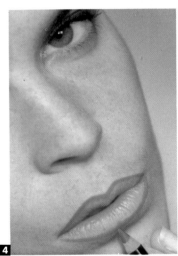

1 *Either: apply very light lipstick and …*

2 *… dab a little highlighter on the centre of the lips – that makes them look larger!*

3 *Or: powder the lips, so that the lipstick adheres well, then …*

4 *… draw a very clean contour line with a dark lip pencil as far outwards as possible (but under no circumstances on the outer side of the lips)!*

5 *Do not use a colour that is too dark for the lips themselves. Lip gloss applied over lipstick also has an enlarging effect.*

FULL LIPS

Perfect emphasis of full lips is better than making them look smaller

Full and beautifully vibrant lips are sensuous and always fashionable. With full lips just avoid gloss and very bright colours.

1 *This looks terrific: lips stained with an outline pencil only look beautifully matt.*
2 *Professionals can do it, but for amateurs it is difficult: to draw the outline far enough inwards so the lips appear a little smaller.*
3 *If the outline is too hard or too thick, soften it with a cotton wool bud. This often suffices as complete lip make-up.*
4 *A great effect, but not easy even for professionals: to make the lip contours look softer use a white or concealer pencil. Blend the white into the foundation with a clean lip brush.*

FRECKLES

Don't hide them under thick make-up!

Bleaching is long since taboo. But covering freckles up is no help. Either the freckles show through, making the face look dirty, or the foundation has to be so thick that the skin looks unnatural.

1 *A soft balance between the unmarked and freckled places is achieved by using a foundation that is not too dark, or a light transparent make-up. Often a thin layer of powder is enough.*
2 *Bring a little life to the cheeks and temples with rose-coloured powder blusher.*
3 *For eyeshadow and lipstick choose only pastel tones, and apply all colours so sparingly that the skin shines through. Bright and dark colours usually have a hard effect on freckles.*
4 *One exception: the eyelashes. Carefully apply dark mascara or the eyes will not have enough emphasis.*

PALE SKIN

Do everything to emphasise its beauty!

A pale complexion is fashionable, at least since the serious health warnings concerning tanning. Don't worry: snow white skin is not at all boring if it is emphasised and complemented with the right make-up.

1 *Those with light skin have a tendency to dark shadows under the eyes. These can be covered with a special light cream.*

2 *If the skin is not completely free from blemishes, apply a thin layer of transparent make-up and go over it with pink, then lightly powder. Powder alone should be enough if you have fine pores.*

3 *Apply blusher only as a soft shadow over the cheekbones.*

4 *A great contrast: matt, but darkly made-up and carefully outlined.*

5 *Red brown eyeshadow emphasises pale skin. The same can be achieved with very thin, smokey shadow in violet or grey.*

MAKE-UP WITH GLASSES

Soft shadows are better than lines

How you make-up to your best advantage if you wear glasses depends whether you are long or short-sighted.

1 *The eyes and lids often look unnaturally large behind glasses prescribed for long sight but,*

2 *Glasses for short sight can make the eyes look quite small.*

3 *These magnifying and reducing effects can be minimised by wearing glasses with thinner lenses. Essential for those with long sight: a spherical lens (above) which reduce the apparent size of the eyelid and pupil.*

Make-up that doesn't make the eyes look even larger

The make-up rule that dark colours make shadowed areas look smaller is only partly true with glasses prescribed for long sight. The magnification almost always cancels this out.

1 *Do not use dark lid and kohl lines at all; instead try a softly coloured effect using transparent grey tones.*

2 *Combinations of pastel tones are correct.*

3 *With glasses for long sight care must be taken to ensure that the eyelashes do not stick together.*

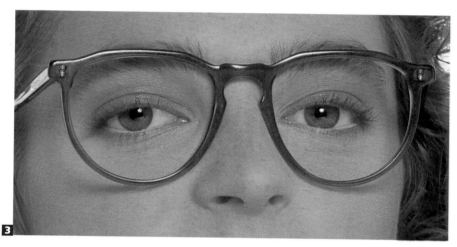

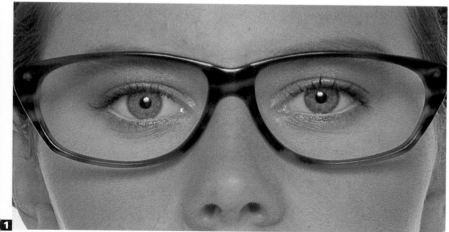

Make-up that doesn't make the eyes look even smaller

Normally light areas stand out. However, behind glasses for short sight, which strongly reduce the size of the eyes, this does not apply. Quite the contrary – the eyes look even less prominent. For this reason use dark colours. However, apply the colours transparently and completely cover the lid. Never draw dark lines.

1 *Shining colours and white kohl enlarge the eyes.*

2 *Apply grey shadow, making it darker above.*

3 *Here brown shadow is applied very lightly, but is extensively across the whole eye area.*

SHAPE OF THE FACE

Hair styles that suit round faces

All styles with narrow sides or contours that help break up the round shape are fine. Not good: bushy hair and hair combed away from the face.

1 *Beautifully feminine: long hair with natural or permanent waves, which does not billow too much.*

2 *Very good: asymmetrical short hair-cuts with contours that break up the cheek surfaces.*

3 *A shoulder-length cut with layers that gently play on the cheeks looks good.*

4 *Curls with a lot of volume should always be asymmetrical and not too long; the contour of the cut should be upwards.*

5 *Long straight hair should also be asymmetrical so that one side falls more strongly into the face and conceals its width. Use gel and a hairdryer to bring the hairline over the forehead.*

6 *With a round face it is best to end a page-boy cut level with the corners of the mouth.*

The best hair styles for triangular faces

The chin does not necessarily need to show, but there should be an optical balance between chin and hair. A half-length cut that ends just above the level of the chin is easiest to manage.

1 *A cut with life at the ends fills out the width missing around the chin. This angular, full cut achieves a good horizontal balance.*

2 *When the locks tumble down to the shoulders a pointed chin is not so noticeable!*

3 *Flick-ups draw attention away from the chin.*

4 *A central parting and the ends blow-dried inwards almost turn the shape of the face upside down and so achieve a balance.*

5 *Asymmetrical locks falling down over the shoulders look nice with any face shape.*

6 *The trick in picture 4 works better with curled or wavy locks.*

Hair styles for square faces

Avoid all styles with hard lines if the face is rather square. Asymmetrical hair cuts that play gently around the face are good and flattering.

1 *Short hairstyles should not sit like a cap on the head, but, as here, should be strongly tapered right down to the fringed layers.*

2 *A good idea: an asymmetrical style which emphasises fullness, and so softens the square contours of the face.*

3 *Here the shape of the face is consciously emphasised, but effectively framed with soft waves.*

4 *Good when the forehead is rather flat and the hairline fairly straight: all the hair should be as full as possible and the fringe tapered forwards.*

5 *The locks fall so far into the face that its square contours are covered.*

6 *The ideal counterpart to a beautiful, clear chin contour: a generous swing of the hair over the forehead.*

If the face is long and narrow..

… then there are really just two possibilities: fullness, with the sides of the hair pushed out a little wider, or contours that effectively break up the effect of the long face.

1 *With short haircuts it is important to have plenty of volume in the outer hair.*
2 *With a narrow face, long hair should not be straight, but curly and tapered.*
3 *Ideal for long faces: a short bob with fringes, with the sides pulled over the cheeks.*
4 *Full locks from ear to ear and a long diagonal fringe balance a long face.*
5 *The hair here is brushed away from the face on one side and towards the face on the other; the uneven distribution enhances the face.*
6 *A decisive style: the roots next to the central parting should be blow-dried high and fixed with spray, and the length must also be right: two fingers width above the chin!*

CHAPTER 6

Make-up for every occasion

- **Look super on the beach**
- **Make-up for the piste**
- **A casual look for the weekend**
- **Colours that stay on in the water**
- **Look pretty when you're training**

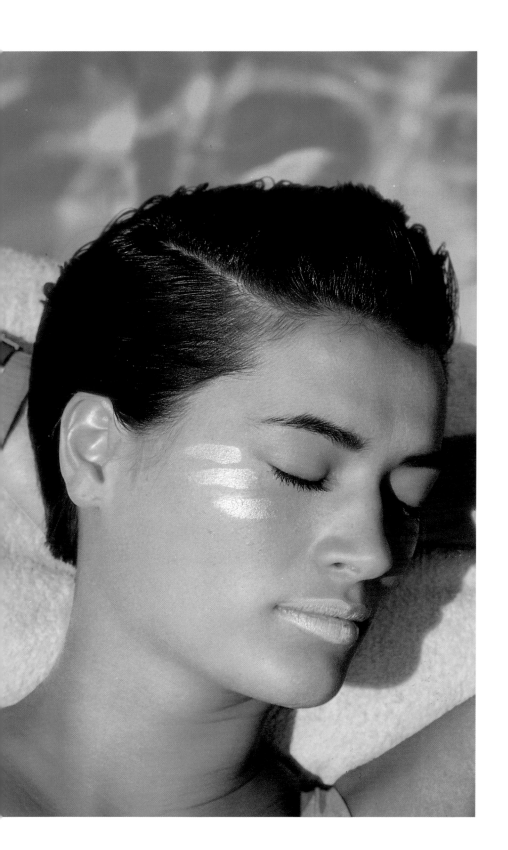

SUNBATHING

Coloured sun block for sensitive areas

Foundation is a good protection against UV rays in daylight, but it is not enough when sunbathing. Besides, it would stop you becoming tanned. Anyone who wants to look crispy brown can apply coloured sun cream. Coloured sun block (also available in green, blue and yellow) can be applied to the lids, the lips and the cheekbones. It looks amusing and also protects against sunburn! Mascara smudges when used with greasy sun protection. It is better to dye the eyelashes (see page 66).

WINTER SPORTS

The cold and sun determine the colour to use

Coloured sun cream creates a crisp brown look, but it makes collars and hoods dirty easily. Better: use self tan and a sun protection cream (with a strong filter). The cold and wind provide a natural blush! Select a lipstick with a blue or yellow tinge which will match the reddened skin. If it does not contain a sun filter, apply a protection cream first. Eyeshadow on the piste is a matter of taste. Be careful with iridescent colours. They do not look attractive in cold winter light and with blue skin.

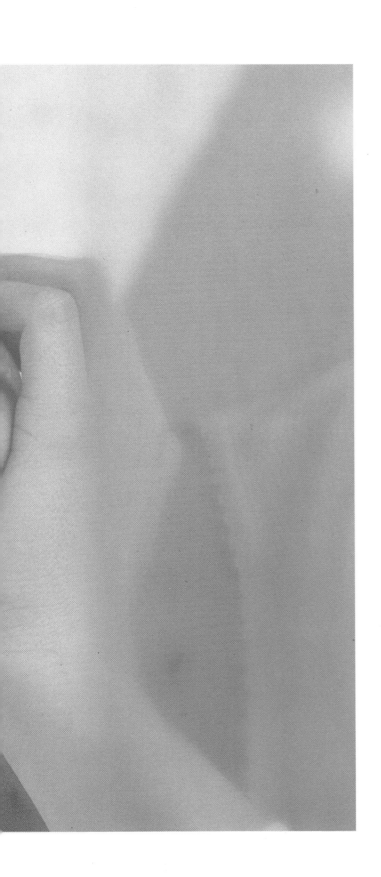

WEEKENDS

This is the time for very little, even no make-up

A suggestion for lazy days with just the two of you. Matt the skin slightly — perhaps with a rosy coloured powder. Apply a brush-stroke of powder blush in a soft rose or salmon colour on cheeks and lids. Enhance the eyes with a dash of dark mascara. Pretty for the lips: a gentle colour, that suits the blush, mixed with lip gloss or Vaseline.

WATER SPORTS

What make-up is suitable for swimming?

Waterproof colours? No problem. Compact make-up – cream blush and cream eyeshadow – even survive a dive, although afterwards they may cling to your towel! Waterproof lipstick and outline sticks are available, as well as mascara. Despite this, use make-up sparingly. Just a coloured eyeline, some mascara and a lipstick that matches the natural colour of the lips – more than this looks inappropriate by the pool.

FITNESS TRAINING

Too much make-up looks un-sporty

In all sports where you sweat alot such as tennis, jogging, light athletics or studio fitness training, you really don't need any make-up - it looks as out of place as does jangly jewellery. Anyone who does a lot of sport is best advised to apply self tan, because it makes the complexion look fresh and the tan doesn't dissolve even when you're exercising at full stretch. Blush is not required, the exercise provides it! Apply mascara to the lashes and dab them with gloss — that's all you need.

acne   97-8
advice   101
allergies   100
ampoule treatments   99, 104
anti-stress programme   104-5
applicators   32-3, 43
autumn type   13, 22-5
        colours for   23-5

blackheads   96, 98
blusher   32-3, 41, 50-53, 78,
                                    81, 86, 89
        application   51-2
        autumn type   23, 24-5
        colour   52-3
        cream   51-2
        powder   51-2
        spring type   15, 16-17
        summer type   19, 20-21
        winter type   29, 28-9
        see also terracotta powder
brushes   32-3, 41-2, 43
buying make-up   37, 100-101

casual make-up   125
cleanser   93, 95, 96
cleansing   92-9
        masks   97, 98
cold, effect on skin 103-4, 123
collagen   73, 101
colour types   12-30
        testing for   12-13
        see also autumn type, spring
        type, summer type, winter
        type
compact foundation 32-3, 35,
                                            41-2
        application   36
compresses   104, 105
contact lenses   55, 66
contouring
        eyes   56, 62-3
        face   48-9, 82
        lips   70, 110-11
cool colours   16, 20
        see also summer type,
        winter type
cosmetic peeling   94, 97, 101
cosmetics see make-up
covering creams   38
covering stick   38

daytime make-up   37

equipment   32-3, 43
evening make-up   37, 39,
                                            80-83
exfoliation   94, 97, 101
eye cream   94, 95, 97
eyebrow pencil   32-3, 79, 86
eyebrows   44-7
        dyeing   46
        fashions in   45
        plucking   45, 46-7
        shape of   45, 46-7, 86
        tattooing   46
        toning   45-7

eyelashes   64-7, 83
        curling   66-7, 83
        dyeing   66
        false   67, 83
        see also mascara
eyelids, hidden   108
eyeliner   32-3, 60-63, 83
        application of   61-3
        autumn type   24-5
        fashions in   61
        spring type   16-17
        summer type   20-21
        winter type   27, 28-9
        see also kohl
eyes
        contouring 56, 62-3, 82-3,
                                    108, 109
        hidden eyelids   108
        make-up removal   93-4
        shadows under   37, 38, 49
        small   109
eyeshadow 32-3, 54-9, 82, 86
        application   55-7, 82
        autumn type   23, 24-5
        colours   58-9
        contouring   56
        ingredients   58
        spring type   15, 16-17
        summer type   19, 20-21
        types of   55
        winter type   27, 28-9
eyeshadow pencil   55

face
        care and cleansing   92-9
        long   73, 119
        masks   94, 95, 97, 98, 99,
                                            104
        round   73, 116
        square   118
        triangular   117
        see also skin
fitness training   127
foundation   33, 34-9, 78, 81,
                                            85
        application   36-8, 78
        autumn type   23, 24-5
        buying   37, 100-101
        colour   36-7
        ingredients   35
        spring type   15, 16
        storage   38-9
        summer type   19, 20-21
        types of   35
        winter type   27, 28-9
        see also contouring,
        powder
foundation cream   35, 36
freckles   15, 24, 112

glasses, effect on make-up
                                            114-5

hair styles   116-19

kohl   32-3, 62-3, 79, 86
        autumn type   24-5

spring type   16-17
summer type   20-21
winter type   27, 28-9
life style   98
lip brush   69, 70-71
lip contour pencil   32-3, 69,
                                    70-71, 73
lip gloss   32-3, 69-71, 73
lip powder   70
lip-proteins   101
lips   68-73
        contouring   70, 110-11
        full   111
        tattooing   73
        thin   110
lipstick   32-3, 68-73, 79, 83,
                                            87
        application   69, 70, 87
        autumn type   23, 24-5,
                                            70-71
        colour   69, 70
        ingredients   69, 72
        spring type   15, 16-17,
                                            70-71
        summer type   19, 20-21,
                                            70-71
        winter type 27, 28-9, 70-71
liquid foundation   35, 36

make-up
        advice   101
        and beauty   8-9
        buying   37, 100-101
        casual   125
        equipment   32-3, 43
        evening   37, 39, 80-83
        and fashion   9
        natural   76-9
        quick make-up   88-9
        removal   92-9
        storage   38-9
        waterproof   126
        work make-up   84-7
make-up sticks   35
mascara   32-3, 65-6, 79, 83,
                                            87
        application   65-7
        autumn type   24-5
        spring type   15, 16-17
        summer type   19, 20-21
        types of   65
        winter type   27, 28-9
massage   104-5
moisturiser   35, 37, 89, 99
moisturising mask   94, 95
mouth   69, 73
natural make-up   76-9
natural moisturising factor
                                            101
neck   38, 51, 99
pH value   101
pores   37, 96, 97-8
powder   40-43, 79
        application   41-2

brushes   32-3, 41-2
coloured   42
compact 32-3, 35, 41-2, 89
ingredients   42
loose   41-2
terracotta   51, 52-3
transparent   32-3, 42, 81,
                                            85
        see also contouring,
        foundation

quick make-up   88-9, 125
regeneration   101
relaxation   104-5
rouge see blusher

seasonal types see colour
types
skin   90-105
        blemished   37-8, 43, 97-8
        care and cleansing   92-9
        dry   92, 94-5
        mature   98-9
        mixed   92-4
        oily   92, 96-7
        pale   113
        protection against cold
                                            103-4
        protection against sun 37,
                                            102-3
        testing   92
soap   93, 96, 101
sponges   32-3, 36, 38
spots   37-8, 96, 97-8
spring type   13, 14-17
        colours for   15-17
stress, effect on skin   104-5
summer type   13, 18-21
        colours for   19-21
sun, effect on skin   37, 102-3,
                                    122, 123
sunbathing   102-3, 122

tattooing
        eyebrows   46
        lips   73
teeth   70
terracotta powder   51, 52-3
toned day cream   35, 37
toner   93, 95, 96
tweezers   32-3, 45, 46-7
UV filter creams 99, 102, 122
vitamins   99
warm colours   16
        see also autumn type,
        spring type
water sports   126
waterproof make-up   126
winter sports   123
winter type   13, 26-9
        colours for   27-9
work make-up   84-7
wrinkles   49, 58, 73, 102

This is your Magic Colour Swatch. Cut out the pages and use them as instructed to find your colour type.

Autumn

This is your Magic Colour Swatch. Cut out the pages and use them as instructed to find your colour type.

Winter

This is your Magic Colour Swatch. Cut out the pages and use them as instructed to find your colour type.

Summer

This is your Magic Colour Swatch. Cut out the pages and use them as instructed to find your colour type.

Spring

This is your Magic Colour Swatch. Cut out the pages and use them as instructed to find your colour type.

Spring/Autumn

This is your Magic Colour Swatch. Cut out the pages and use them as instructed to find your colour type.

Summer/Winter

This is your Magic Colour Swatch. Cut out the pages and use them as instructed to find your colour type.

Summer

This is your Magic Colour Swatch. Cut out the pages and use them as instructed to find your colour type.

Spring

This is your **Magic Colour Swatch**. Cut out the pages and use them as instructed to find your colour type.

Spring

This is your Magic Colour Swatch. Cut out the pages and use them as instructed to find your colour type.

Summer

This is your Magic Colour Swatch. Cut out the pages and use them as instructed to find your colour type.

Winter

This is your Magic Colour Swatch. Cut out the pages and use them as instructed to find your colour type.

Autumn

This is your Magic Colour Swatch. Cut out the pages and use them as instructed to find your colour type.

Autumn

This is your Magic Colour Swatch. Cut out the pages and use them as instructed to find your colour type.

Winter

This is your Magic Colour Swatch. Cut out the pages and use them as instructed to find your colour type.